W9-BOF-905

Karen Ann Quinlan

Dying in the Age of
Eternal Life

Karen Ann Quinlan

Dying in the Age of
Eternal Life

B.D. COLEN

Nash Publishing, New York

Copyright © 1976 by B. D. Colen

All rights reserved. No part of this book may be reproduced in any form or by any means without permission in writing from the publisher

Nash Publishing Corporation
1 Dupont Street
Plainview, N.Y. 11803

Portions of this book have appeared in various forms in *The Washington Post*. Material is used with permission.

Quotation of Stewart Alsop from *Stay of Execution*, copyrighted 1973 by J.B. Lippincott Co., reprinted by permission of J.B. Lippincott Co.

Library of Congress Catalog Card Number: 76-7144
International Standard Book Number: 0-8402-1368-9

Printed in the United States of America
Second Printing

For Sara, Benjamin, and my parents, who have provided me with enough joy in living to carry me through an examination of dying.

CONTENTS

Preface 9
Acknowledgments 13

Part One: Karen Ann Quinlan
1   In Some Ways, It's Harder Now 19
2   I Just Couldn't Do It 29

Part Two: The Problem
3   Whose Dignity? Whose Death? 47

Part Three: The Saviors and the Saved
4   We'll Keep the Electrons Snapping 67
5   This Unit Plays God Every Time It Saves
     Somebody 85

Part Four: The Infants
6   There Is No Wrong Decision 105
7   Diagnostically, She's a Freak of Nature 123

Part Five: The Will to Live and the Living Will
8   I Will Not Play God! 141
9   Can't They Stop and Let Him Die? 159
10   I Can't Die Yet, the Washing Isn't Caught Up! 173
11   I Want to Die in This Bed! 183

Afterword 201
Index 203

PREFACE

This is not a book about the substance of Karen Ann Quinlan's life. It is, instead, a book about the meaning of her dying and death. For Karen Ann's life cannot tell us anything we need to know to understand her death, and it is her death, or at least the public nature of her death, that will be of lasting significance. Thousands and thousands of words have already been devoted to Karen Ann and her life before the night of April 14-15, 1975. In those stories the daughter of Joseph Thomas and Julia Quinlan has been portrayed as a shy, sweet, devout young lady—the sort of daughter who populated the fondest dreams of American mothers 15 years ago. And those stories seem to have been based in part on truth and in part on the fondest dreams of Karen Ann's mother. There were also stories about another Karen Ann, a good-girl-gone-bad, who had left her church, left her parents' home, and had spent her last conscious day popping pills and downing gin and tonic. Those accounts also seem to have been based in part on truth, in part on the reports of some who called themselves Karen's friends, and in part on unfounded rumor and gossip.

9

In reality, Karen Ann Quinlan appears to have been an amalgamation of the "good" Karen and the "bad" Karen. For in the last quarter of the 20th century there are few 21-year-old women who would fit Julia Quinlan's description of her daughter. Yet blood tests administered to Karen the night of her admission to Newton Memorial Hospital, Newton, N.J., belie reports that she had been popping pills all day prior to lapsing into a coma. The tests did confirm stories that she had been drinking gin and tonic for there were traces of quinine in her blood. She also had taken some Valium and Librium—two of the most commonly prescribed tranquilizers—for traces of those too were found. But the drugs were well within the limits of "therapeutic" dosage. Karen did not have a prescription for the pills; and while that might provide us with an object lesson about the dangers of mixing pills and alcohol, in this nation of drug abusers it neither sets Karen Ann Quinlan apart from her peers nor tells us anything about her that had any bearing on her parents' decision to allow her to die.

During the months I have followed the Quinlan case, both for *The Washington Post* and in the preparation of this book, I made no serious attempt to delve into Karen Ann's background. Not that I wasn't curious about the young woman whose name has become a sort of shorthand symbol describing a particular state of being, but I felt in the beginning, and still feel, that focusing on "Karen the person" only detracts attention from the vitally important issues raised by the case. As Daniel Coburn, the attorney who was appointed to represent Karen Ann's best interests, said in his summation in the New Jersey Superior Court: " . . . You can't use a quality-of-life argument based on what someone looks like, any more than you can go back into Karen's background.

"I am saying this in all respect to the family, but it is a point that has to be made. There have been all sorts of discussions as to what caused this [coma]. It makes no difference at all whether this was caused by lead poisoning, from her job, from falling in her home, from a drug overdose; Karen is in this condition today. Medically it might have some significance, but legally it has none.

"As to her lifestyle before this, it makes no difference whether she was the Virgin Mary, or Mary Magdalene. It is of no consequence at all. . . ."

What is of immense personal consequence, however, is the effect Karen Ann Quinlan's illness has had on those around her and the effect it has had, and might eventually have, on the development of the law and practice of medicine. Obviously, the case has had the most direct and dramatic impact on Joe and Julia Quinlan and their two other children, 17-year-old John and 19-year-old Mary Ellen, who first had to live with the realization that their daughter and sister was deathly ill, then with the fact that she would never recover, then with the painful thought that they wanted her to die, and finally, with the fact that Karen Ann's physicians insisted upon making her a prisoner of medical technology. What has been for some people a challenging legal exercise and has for others been the focus of an ivory tower debate, has, for the Quinlan family, been a supreme test of their religious faith, of their belief in the humanity of man, and of their belief in their own ability to cope with the type of dilemma most of us encounter only in our worst nightmares.

But the Quinlans are far from being the first parents who have had to decide that life-sustaining care should be withdrawn from a beloved child or any other family member for that matter. As you will read in the following pages, the only thing unusual about the Quinlans' ordeal was the publicity attending it. While that publicity has caused the Quinlans great pain, making them martyrs of the same technology that imprisoned their daughter, their martyrdom will not be in vain if it serves to make us all aware that we do not have ten years, or even ten weeks, to debate and ruminate over the question of whether, at some point in the future, hopelessly ill patients should be allowed to die. For decisions are being made every day to withhold life-sustaining care from dying patients. What we must now decide is whether these decisions are being carefully made by the proper persons and whether they are being implemented in such a way that the rights of patient, family, and physiciar are protected.

B. D. COLEN
WASHINGTON, D.C.
JULY 26, 1976

ACKNOWLEDGMENTS

I wish to thank my editors at *The Washington Post,* Howard Simons, Leonard Downie, Jr., Herbert Denton, and Kevin Klose, for their willingness to allow me to cover a subject long neglected by the media—the problems relating to dying and death—as well as for their encouragement while working on this project. Thanks also to Michael Hill, Mark Olshaker, Dr. Bennett Olshaker, Donald J. Colen, and my wife, Sara Colen, for their many helpful suggestions and criticisms. Thanks also to my agent, Edward J. Acton, for keeping me on the right track, and special thanks to Douglas Feaver and John Severance.

"A dying man needs to die, as a sleepy man needs to sleep, and there comes a time when it is wrong, as well as useless, to resist."

Stewart Alsop, *Stay of Execution*

Part One

KAREN ANN QUINLAN

1

In Some Ways, It's Harder Now

"The committee considered the Supreme Court opinion in In Re Quinlan, heard Dr. Richard Watson, Mr. and Mrs. Quinlan, Fr. Trapasso, and Meredythe L. Nansen, who's assistant director of nursing at Morris View. The committee is unanimously of the opinion that Karen Quinlan is presently in a coma, and is in a chronic, persistent, vegetative state. The committee is unanimously of the opinion that Mr. Quinlan, as guardian and parent of Karen Quinlan, Mrs. Quinlan, as Karen's mother, and Dr. Watson, as Karen Quinlan's responsible attending physician agree, that there is no reasonable possibility of Karen ever emerging from her present, comatose, condition, to a cognitive, sapient state. The committee unanimously agrees with this opinion . . . ."

Donald L. Berlin, counsel to the Morris County (N.J.) Welfare Board, announcing the decision of the Morris View Nursing Home's ethics committee's decision in regard to Karen Ann Quinlan.

Three hours after Berlin's announcement, Joseph Thomas Quinlan sat slumped in an easy chair in the Quinlans' family room, a cold beer in his hand and a smile on his face. "You know," he told me, "this is the first time since

September when I can really relax. It feels great. I know she's being properly taken care of and that machine won't be pushing air back and forth into her when there isn't any hope. The monitor is gone, which they had until the day [she was transferred to Morris View from St. Clare's Hospital]. Wasn't that silly? They had the monitor and a nurse watching it. Then they had another alarm on the trachea in case she should cough anything up."

It had been a long fight for Joe and Julia Quinlan, a fight they had lost and had won many times over. First they were told they weren't their daughter's guardians, so they had to ask a court to allow them to have her respirator turned off. Then the New Jersey Superior Court denied their historic petition. However, the New Jersey Supreme Court granted their request and, in an opinion which the Quinlans believed marked the end of their public ordeal, ruled that neither guardians nor physicians are legally obligated to sustain the life of a comatose patient with no hope of recovering. But then St. Clare's Hospital and doctors Robert Morse and Arshad Javed once again stood in the Quinlans' way. More than two full months after the Supreme Court ruled, the physicians and hospital finally got around to announcing publicly that they would not allow Karen's death at St. Clare's. The physicians had finally taken Karen off the respirator and had moved her to a private room from the intensive care unit where she had lain for more than a year, but they did not tell the public that Karen Ann Quinlan was still receiving extraordinary care including round-the-clock, private-duty nursing, constant turning, massive doses of antibiotics, and high calorie feedings. She was, said the physicians, healthy, a statement which they and the Quinlans knew to be patently untrue.

Until Karen's transfer to Morris View, June 9, 1976, her family had to suffer in the name of mercy and St. Clare's adherence to the "irreversible tenet to protect life." But

Donald Berlin's announcement on the bright, steaming afternoon of June 10, 1976, finally did mark the beginning of the end, the point at which Joe and Julia Quinlan could stop fighting and start grieving. At that point, the battle was won. They had found a physician and a nursing home that agreed with them that there is no point in prolonging the dying of the already dead. Their daughter Karen Ann was finally freed from machines and monitors so that she might die naturally. And the Quinlans could once again, as they had said they would after the Supreme Court decision in March, withdraw into the circle of their family to do their grieving in the privacy which had been denied them for almost 14 months.

□

Before Karen Ann Quinlan is finally laid to rest in her plot in the Gates of Heaven Cemetery in Hanover, N.J., Father Thomas Trapasso will take the pulpit to speak of Karen and of the lessons we may learn through her dying and her death. Father Tom, as the short, balding priest is known to the Quinlans, his other parishioners, and all who come in contact with him, has had a good deal of time to think about those lessons. For it was he to whom Joe and Julia Quinlan turned during their months of agony. It was he who provided them with spiritual guidance, human warmth, and friendship. And it was he, more than any other person, who had a chance to observe them closely as they reacted to one crisis after another.

Father Tom said, as we sat and talked on the screened-in porch of the rectory of Our Lady of the Lake Church, that he had come to feel there are two basic issues "that surround Karen's case. Number one is the whole idea of technology and medicine and the prolongation of life, and through her [Karen] our whole society has come to discuss this in a way

it was never able to before, and this has resulted in a
workable decision, at least for the people of New Jersey. And
the other thing—Divine Providence—has always been a
problem for me; but I wonder if there's a reason why Karen
survived off the respirator, because it did create another
aspect to the case—the care of the chronic patient. For a-
while it seemed that nobody wanted her—which would have
been horrendous to me—and that doctors would have said,
'well, we saved her life; now somebody take care of her
because we don't want her.' It would have been terrible if
nobody had wanted her. I would never be for euthanasia, but
if anything will open the door for euthanasia, it won't be
mercy killing but the unwanted sick, the burdensome sick;
and our society has to be prepared to care for all the sick.

"Maybe it's very significant that a government agency
[Morris View, the county's nursing home for the indigent]
took over Karen's care. It's a big plus that our society,
symbolically through this Morris County agency, was able to
say, 'yes, we'll take care of Karen and people like her.' So
those two main themes, from the social point of view, are the
two things I would try to get across; that things worked out
in a way that there was the whole question of the
prolongation of life and technology (and we got to that and
sort of solved that problem) and then immediately she
became another problem, in the sense of being a chronic case,
and society came to grips with that."

"What's going to happen to the Quinlans six months
after Karen dies?" I asked Father Trapasso. "Are they going
to fall apart?"

"That's a good question. I haven't thought it all the way
through yet," replied the priest, whose own hair turned
grayer as the case progressed, just as Joseph Quinlan's
eyebrows turned from barely gray to white. "I will be
available to them as they need me. I hope they're in touch
with their own feelings. I don't know how I can do that.

Sometimes I get a little concerned whether or not. . . ." He paused to reflect. "I said at the beginning that I couldn't make decisions for them. They have to ultimately live with it.

"In a way. . . the whole question of Karen surviving off the respirator, . . . could immediately become a great relief to them. . . . Because no matter how much you can theologize about how you don't have to prolong life by extraordinary means, emotionally, if there was a very direct and immediate death occurring from removing the respirator—that in a sense has been removed from them now," Father Tom told me. "Just as the doctor who turns the respirator off is in a different emotional position from the doctor who never turned it on because he thought it was hopeless. So from that point of view, I think they have been relieved of alot of the anxiety that they might have had if Karen had died within days, or even hours, of turning off the respirator. It's all well and good to say in black and white they made a morally correct decision, but whether they could handle it emotionally and psychologically. . . but I think that at this point, in a very real sense, she's been returned to nature. So if she dies of pneumonia, or some infection, it's really nature unfolding. So I think that's really been a blessing for them, and it's something I might mention in the sermon. They really have been relieved of the burden of seeing her death as somehow immediately linked to their decision.

"I think that even now," said Father Tom, about three weeks after Karen had been taken off the respirator, "if Karen dies, they'll be in much the same position as any parent who looses a child through an illness or whatever. I think maybe God has been very good to them in that respect. That was always my fear, that Karen would have died, as we anticipated, when the machine was turned off, and there'd always be that emotional tie, 'we made the decision and she died.' I think the whole thing would have been alot easier to

cope with if it had been immediate, if the doctors had said
after a week, 'there is no hope.' But after 14 months of it and
to then say at that point, 'let's turn it off and let her die,'
there would be alot of emotional complications that could
result from it. And now they're spared that. They've never
verbalized it. And now I realize that if there is a divine plan,
the Lord brought them to the point where society came to
grips with the issue and faced it as best it could at this point
in time and then relieved them of the decision-making at this
point. I think it's very Providential, because in the beginning,
when they first began to talk about this, my prayer was really
that they'd never have to make the decision. And after
[Judge Robert] Muir's [Jr.] decision, I thought they'd never
have to face it."

□

"This is the first victory we've had all along, if you can
call it a victory," Joe Quinlan told me on the morning of
April 1, 1976, 350 days after Karen became comatose. "I
kept thinking all along maybe I heard wrong," Joe continued,
recounting his having been told the day before that the New
Jersey Supreme Court had ruled in his favor. The family was
at peace that morning, as we sat around the kitchen table
drinking coffee. It finally looked as though Karen Ann would
be taken off the respirator and nature would be allowed to
take its course. Joe and Julie, as Julia Quinlan is known to
her friends, had no idea that day that they would have to
struggle for 10 weeks to have the decision implemented, that
they would eventually have to find new doctors and another
health care facility in which to place Karen. That morning
the battle seemed to be over, and they could allow
themselves the luxury of reflection.

"This morning was a little different," Joe said, telling
me of his visit to Karen in the hospital, a visit he and his wife
made twice every day. "We're doing what she would want. It

was a little easier today. She was more peaceful this morning, and that always helps. . . . I always pray for her. I always put my hand on her head to see if she has a temperature and then I pray for her."

"In some ways, it's harder now," said Julie Quinlan, who sat in her pink-and-white-checked bathrobe, quietly stroking Pinky, the family cat, who nestled in Julie's lap. "Now we're finally faced with the reality that she will die. I don't want to say it will be a relief. . . ." Joe started to say something, but Julie continued, "but it will be a relief to see Karen finally released from all the machines she's hooked up to. Someone asked me yesterday if I thought there was some chance she'd recover," Julie said. "We wouldn't have gone through this if we thought that."

Julie and Joe Quinlan knew Karen would not recover for they had seen her. They had watched her as her weight had dropped from 120 to about 70 pounds. They had seen her strong, athletic limbs wither to skin-covered sticks that were drawn against her body and frozen by calcium deposits so they would never move again. She looked like a bizarre praying mantis, with a respirator tube protruding from her throat as a pin would hold an insect specimen in a collection box. She had not spoken to anyone during those months in the intensive care unit, nor had she been aware of the nurse and doctors caring for her. She moved, frequently, but only in the mindless way in which Priestley's frogs moved. She moaned, but only because the involuntary movements of her vocal cords played tricks with the air her respirator and lungs had forced through her throat. Her eyelids would flutter and open, and her eyes roll from side to side, but one would roll left as the other rolled right, and neither saw her mother and father as they made their pilgrimages to her bedside, just as her ears did not hear her mother as she spoke to Karen, prayed to God that Karen would die, and said goodnight to Karen every night

I asked Karen's parents what, up to that point, had been the hardest thing for them to bear.

"The bad publicity has been," replied Julie. She was referring particularly to newspaper articles which portrayed Karen as a hard-drinking, pill-popping, wild young woman and to the publicity attending the state attorney general's fruitless, grand jury inquiry into the question of whether Karen had become comatose after meeting with foul play — a possibility ruled out by local prosecutors and physicians long before the case even went to court.

Joe said the hardest part for him, "after making the decision, was being told I had to go to court. There hasn't been anything private about this all along."

"We will keep our final hours very private," said Julie, "just for the family and priest." She thought, as we spoke, that she and her husband would be withdrawing from public view until Karen's funeral.

Karen's 19-year-old sister, Mary Ellen, said that she too found going through the Superior Court trial was one of the hardest parts of the ordeal. But "the hardest thing for me was the things that were unnecessary, like the attorney general's investigation. I knew right from the start they weren't going to find anything.

"I didn't really understand at first why we were going to turn off the machine," Mary Ellen told me, "it was kind of a shock when it was first suggested." Oddly enough, however, Mary Ellen was the first member of the family to give up hope of Karen's recovery. She may also have been the last family member to see a glimmer of Karen Ann Quinlan in the body lying in St. Clare's Hospital. It happened, she told me, only a few days after Karen became comatose. "It happened when I went down to Newton Memorial Hospital one morning. They always said to talk to her. I had called her name before and nothing happened. She had these dead eyes. But I called 'Karen,' and she looked at me. It just happened once. I stayed down there until 10:30 at night, but she didn't look at me again. I thought that was sad because she was my sister. But it was about the saddest thing in the world that could happen to Karen, she was always so full of life. She sounded like an elephant in the house, even though she was only 5′ 2½″. We used to have a bet who would reach 5′3″ first," said Mary Ellen. "Neither of us ever made it."

2

I Just Couldn't Do It

It all began for the Quinlans with a telephone call at
2:00 A.M. on April 15, 1975. "The nurse in the intensive care
unit at Newton Memorial Hospital called to notify us," Julie
Quinlan told me. "Karen was living with friends in Byram
township. . . . They hadn't realized that she had actually
passed out, and when they realized that she wasn't breathing,
they called the police, and the ambulance came. They rushed
her to the hospital."

There are two basic versions of the events of that night,
just as there are two basic descriptions of Karen's personality
and behavior. In one of the versions, Karen, who had been
drinking heavily, started to pass out at a friend's birthday
party at a nearby bar. Another friend took Karen home, put
her to bed, and a few minutes later realized she wasn't
breathing and called the police. According to the other
version, Karen had already left the party and gone home, had
told friends she wasn't feeling well, and went upstairs to bed.
Her friends checked on her a little while later and, when they
discovered she wasn't breathing, called the police. Julie
Quinlan believed the second, Sleeping Beauty, story or at
least that was the one she told. It is also the story which

29

creates the biggest mystery, for it gives no clue to the cause of Karen's coma.

"What did the doctors tell you, that first night?" I asked the Quinlans.

"They didn't know anything," Julie replied. "She was. . . .they felt she was in a coma at the time, and there hasn't been any communication from the first time we saw her."

"What did the doctors test for?"

"They tested everything," she said. "They tested the blood and the urine and did a brain scan and an angiogram [which involves injecting a dye into the blood stream and then taking a low level X-ray of a particular organ, in this case the brain, to watch the circulation of the dye], every test. We exhausted every test, and every test was negative."

The experts who testified at the trial said they believed Karen's brain damage was caused by a lack of oxygen, and that the damage was completely irreversible. But they do not know what caused her to stop breathing. Those treating her knew only that they were getting nowhere in their attempts to cure her. Instead, she was getting progressively worse. Within days of her admission to the hospital she began to assume the posture she now displays: arms drawn up underneath her in a configuration which Dr. Sidney Diamond, a professor of neurology at New York's Mt. Sinai School of Medicine, described during the trial as "making one tight sort of fetal position. It's too grotesque, really, to describe in human terms like fetal."

And day after day, throughout the late spring and summer, Joe and Julie visited Karen Ann twice a day in the intensive care unit of St. Clare's Hospital in Denville, N.J., where she had been transferred soon after April 15. They would talk to her, pray for her, and Julie would wipe Karen's feverish brow and kiss her, hoping against hope that Karen would respond. But she did not.

"When did you begin to think it was time to turn off the respirator," I asked the couple, as we sat in their living room one evening about a week after they filed their complaint in Superior Court.

"Well, we didn't reach the decision at the same time," replied Julie, who appeared to be taking the lead in the conversation. "I reached the decision before my husband did. First, you have to realize that she isn't going to live. Once you've accepted the fact that she's going to die, then you can start thinking along different lines. But it was a very difficult conclusion to reach. In the beginning we had hoped that. . . ."

"We had alot of hope," Joe said quietly, to no one in particular.

". . . that perhaps she would come out of the coma," continued Julie. "But as we saw the brain damage progressing we realized there just wasn't any hope."

"I'm sure that with the mechanism [the respirator] she could continue in the state she's in," Joe said, "but that's not really living. She's just a vegetable."

"When did you come to the conclusion that it was hopeless and accept it?"

"I don't really know the exact time," Julie said and then indicated it might have been about a month before the court case was filed. "I really don't know exactly. But, you know, when you visit her every day and see she's actually returning to the fetal position. And you know you realize that there's just absolutely no hope at all. And then you realize that it's best if God just takes her."

"You go to see her every day?"

"We both go twice a day," Julie replied.

"Why?" I asked.

"Why do I go every day?" Julie repeated the question, looking at me as though I were slightly crazy for having asked it. ". . . I don't know if I could really answer something like that."

"Simply because she's our child and we love her," Joe cut in, picking up the conversation. "She's lying there helpless. Nobody can do anything for her. We just want to see her as much as possible."

"I don't think I could go to bed at night without seeing her, without knowing she's still alive," Julie said, having gathered her thoughts. "Just like saying goodnight to, you know, to your other two children. I don't believe that I could go to bed without saying something to her too. It's kind of a strange situation...." She paused before continuing, "I don't think I've really given it any thought. But when you go down there and you talk to her, [it's] because she's still there. And she's probably more precious to us now than she's ever been. You know, when you love someone you want to see them as often as you can because you don't know how much longer you will be able to touch her and talk to her...."

"But how can you continue to go, watching her deteriorate this way?"

"I think we've sort of been worrying about each other and worrying about each other—" said Joseph Quinlan, who looked as though he couldn't stand much more worrying about anyone.

"You sound as though you're very torn," I said to Julie at one point.

"I guess that's just a mother's love," she responded. "I can still touch her, you know. I can still feel her. That's the difference. There's no response. I'll stand there and talk to her, but there's no response. But she's still alive to the extent [that she's there]."

"But you speak of her as a vegetable, as being dead, and yet you continue to visit her. Why," I asked again.

"I don't know if I can answer that. If ... death is final, this isn't final; she's still there. Maybe I am going in two directions. But as long as she's there I'll continue to go down. In some ways, death is easier to deal with because then you accept the fact that she just isn't any more. So this is more of a physical and emotional strain because it's been going on and on. It'll be 22 weeks, so it's really a drain on everyone."

(As this is being written, it has been 14 months, and "it's still going on.")

Joe Quinlan, too, spoke of visiting Karen. "You know she's not going to get well," he said, "but one time she'll have a good night in that she won't be moving so much. And other times she'll have a bad night where she's moving an awful lot in the bed to the point where she just wore the skin right off her face, you know, from rubbing up against the pillow all night long. And no matter what kind of mood we find her in, we walk away from the hospital kind of depressed. If she's in a good state, then of course we don't feel like leaving, we want to be with her. And then, if she's having a bad night, we don't want to leave either."

"Do her facial expressions change?"

"Only, I'd say. . . it would remind you of an expression of pain," said Joe who was pained himself by the memory. "All the doctors keep on assuring us that she's not in pain because that part of the brain is damaged. . . . But it's just like someone would grimace when they're in terrible pain."

(A month later, at the trial, neurologists would describe Karen Ann's so-called "expressions" as "stereotyped" or "patterned" reflexes caused by the autonomous nervous system rather than by emotions or, for that matter, a conscious awareness of pain. Each time Karen moves a certain way, or is poked or pinched in a certain way, that movement or stimulus sets off a patterned response which is identical each time it is triggered.)

I turned the conversation back to Julia Quinlan's realization that her daughter was not going to recover and to the decisions which followed from that realization. "Did you say anything to your husband when you gave up?"

"No, I didn't say anything to him. I was very cautious what I'd say to him because he hadn't reached that point. I had discussed it with Father Tom, but it's something you must reach your own decision on. It isn't something you can talk someone into. So I had to be very careful what I said to Joe."

"Eventually I came to the same decision," Joe said, explaining that he too came to believe it was pointless—nay, cruel—to attempt to keep Karen alive indefinitely as an appendage of the respirator.

"When did you reach that conclusion," I asked.

"I don't know. Much later than the rest of them. It must have been a couple of weeks. I just couldn't believe she wouldn't get better, because we've never had anything like this in all the years we've been married. Every time someone got sick it seemed like all that we had to do was pray, and they got better. It took a little time to resolve myself to the fact that she was going to . . ." He paused, and there seemed to be tears in his eyes. ". . .that we were going to lose her.

"Once I reached the point when I realized there wasn't any hope . . . it was the only thing to do, really [turning off the respirator] . . . . The toughest part was realizing that she wasn't going to live. Once you reached that point, it just naturally followed that this would be the next thing."

But what seemed natural to Joe and Julie Quinlan did not, in the age of eternal life, malpractice suits, and the Edelin case, seem natural to either the two relatively young physicians treating Karen or to the officials of St. Clare's Hospital.

Joe Quinlan swears to this day, as he swore under oath in court, that it was Dr. Arshad Javed, the pulmonary internist providing Karen's respiratory care, who first broached the subject of turning off the respirator. Dr. Javed swore under oath that he had only suggested an attempt be made to "wean" Karen off the machine. And Joe Quinlan told the court of a series of meetings with doctors and hospital officials, meetings at which the Quinlans say they were first lead to believe that their request would be granted: first if a precedent could be found for doing so; then if they would sign a consent form; then if they would have themselves appointed Karen's guardians. By the time the case was heard, things had deteriorated to the point where both Dr. Morse, the neurologist attending Karen, and Dr. Javed testified they would resist judicially granted authorization to turn off the machine.

What Joseph Quinlan, a simple, honest man, did not understand is that decisions to cease treatment are neither simple nor honest. They are made by family, or physicians, with very little discussion. They are based, for the most part, upon unspoken understandings. They are not reached in hospital conference rooms, with parents, siblings, physicians, parish priests, hospital chaplains and hospital administrators present—as was the case in the Quinlan discussions. Rather, they are secret decisions leading up to secret actions of questionable legality. They are decisions that are virtually never recorded in official records. They are decisions made and acted upon every day, but rerely, if ever, are they acted upon in the open, honest, logical way in which Joseph Quinlan assumed such things are done.

I asked the couple if they could have made their decision and fought for its implementation without the support of their religion and religious faith.

"I think it would have been more difficult to reach the decision if we weren't religious," said Julie Quinlan, who worked regularly as a secretary in the offices of Our Lady of the Lake, Father Trapasso's church in Mt. Arlington, N.J. "And I think that if we didn't pray about it, I don't think I could have reached the decision."

"Right along," Joe Quinlan replied, "this decision seemed so natural. Everything was natural all the way along.

When we finally realized" that Karen would never recover, the idea of turning off the respirator "seemed like it would normally follow. Because we were told by all the doctors the case was hopeless, it just naturally followed that we should turn off the machine and put her back in her natural state.

"Could we have made the decision if we weren't religious? I know that religion was a great source of strength and comfort. What I meant was that it just naturally followed that there was nothing else we could do."

"But isn't part of your willingness to do this in part based on your feeling that you're simply freeing her from the sorrows of this life for a better one? Would you be more inclined to hang on if you didn't believe in that better life," I asked.

"I see . . . . It might have made a difference, yes. We might have tried to hold on to her . . . . It's tough though, to try to put yourself in someone else's place. I just can't picture myself not having any beliefs," Joe said. "It doesn't seem like there's much of a purpose to life if you don't have something to believe in."

During the trial, the attorney opposing Joseph Quinlan's request tried to make it seem as though he had been talked into his position by Father Trapasso and the Roman Catholic Church. As Father Trapasso testified, the Church does not consider it morally obligatory to continue life-prolonging treatment for a patient for whom the treatment is not prolonging life but is only prolonging death. Indeed, one of the Quinlans' basic legal arguments was that their Constitutional right to practice their religion was being interfered with by those preventing them from turning off Karen Ann's respirator. But Joseph Quinlan would not have his words twisted, would not be pushed around, and he continued to insist that both he and his Church had arrived independently, centuries apart, at the same logical conclusion.

"Were you at all surprised," I asked during a conversation after the trial, "that the decision you made happened to be in the line with the Church's teachings on withholding care?"

"Not surprised, not really surprised. I tell you, I was a little relieved though."

"That you weren't in conflict with the Church? "'

"Right, that there was no conflict," replied Joe Quinlan, a man whom one instinctively feels has known without a doubt, for the greater part of his half century, what is right and what is wrong, and a man who has little use for the grays between black and white.

There is a story that Joe Quinlan can sometimes be persuaded to tell which says a great deal about his character, his basic morality, and the manner in which he makes a decision like the one involving the disconnection of Karen Ann's respirator, the kind of decision with which we are faced only a few times in our lives, if at all.

"I was only 19 when I learned the difference between moral law and man's law," he said, as he began the story he had resisted retelling.

It was 1944, and Joe, who later lost a hand in the Battle of the Bulge, was serving with the U.S. Army in Germany. "Our battalion moved into a town and was immediately cut off," he remembered, "so we were in that town for about a week, 10 days, completely cut off. And during that time there were counterattacks going on day and night. At one time me and another young man were told to go out and shoot. . ." Here Joe hesitated. His voice was barely audible, and his head was lowered so he was staring at the table at which we sat. ". . . shoot a bunch of prisoners, there were about 20 of them lined up, sitting on the ground."

"Were they civilians, or German soldiers, or what?"

"German soldiers. It's not something you're too proud of, you know. Some of the things you're told to do in time

of war, even by your own side . . . . But me and another
young man were told to take our turn guarding the prisoners,
and while we were, a major came out of a building. He was
the C.O. and he came over to the two of us and he said he
had received word that there was to be a counterattack that
night, and he didn't want 'these S.O.B.s'—the
prisoners—running around loose.' Then, just to make sure
there was no doubt in our minds, he said, 'if the Germans
attack I want you to kill every one of them.'

"Even at 19," Joe Quinlan said, "I knew two things
immediately: that it was illegal and immoral; and that I
couldn't do it under any circumstances, not unarmed
prisoners who were no threat to me or anyone else. So any
way, to make a long story short, I did alot of praying. The
other fellow was sitting on something, with like a submachine
gun, and he was watching the prisoners. I had a carbine and I
walked the length of the line down to the other end of the
prisoners and back and forth, and I did alot of praying while
I walked for those few hours. I just prayed that I wouldn't
have to make the decision. I knew I couldn't do it anyway,
and I just prayed the Lord would make the decision for me,
take it out of my hands completely."

"You made the decision hoping you wouldn't have to
act on it?"

"I knew I couldn't do it," Joe continued, "but to
refuse could have meant a death penalty. In time of war you
wouldn't even need a court martial. I mean, the major could
come out of there and pull out his pistol and that would be
the end of it. And he would have been justified under
military law to do it as an example to the rest of the men. I
prayed alot," Joe said. And there is no question that he did.
"Anyway, we were relieved after a few hours by a couple of
young men and we passed down to the men what the major
said about the counterattack. We did not tell them what he
said about the prisoners. And the attack took place that night

and the major was shot. He was coming down the steps of the building, and one of the stray bullets hit him, and he fell all the way down the steps; so he was out of the picture. The two young men who were guarding the prisoners got them all together, put them in a building, like they should have, and guarded them until the attack was over. Then, the next morning, that is just the way I found them, sitting on the top of the basement steps with the prisoners all down below. That was quite an order to give a couple of young men," Joe Quinlan said, thinking about that decision he made 10 years before Karen was born.

"I couldn't obey an order like that. I just couldn't do it. I would have probably tried to explain my way out of it. At that age you think of all different things. I was thinking that the other young man would do it, and when he did I could fire over their heads, and then I'd get out of it. But that wasn't practical because he would have . . . that would have been giving the o.k. to the act and that would have been wrong too. So I was stuck, and that's why I did alot of praying. The point I'm trying to make is I knew immediately it was something I couldn't do."

"Where as once you realized Karen wouldn't recover you knew turning off the respirator would be right?"

"That I know is right. All that mattered was it took me a little longer to realize that it was going to happen, that we were going to lose her and to give up hope for her surviving. It took me a little longer than the rest of the family, but once I reached that point, there was no doubt."

During their press conferences, public appearances, and most interviews, Joe and Julie Quinlan have repeatedly referred to their daughter in the past tense, as though she were already dead. They have, as was mentioned earlier, called her a vegetable and have, in fact, said they consider her to be dead. But during the course of several lengthy conversations with Joe and Julie, both before and after the trial, it became increasingly clear to me that no matter how convinced they were intellectually that they were doing the right thing, emotionally they were very unsure of themselves.

"Would it make it easier for you," I asked the couple the day after Judge Robert Muir, Jr., released his opinion, "if you could just say to yourselves, 'Karen is dead,' and stop going to the hospital?"

"No," Julie replied, shaking her head slowly. "We could never do that. I don't wish to do that, either."

"Through all of this, in going through the trial, and all the publicity, did you ever consider just going into the room yourself one night to disconnect the respirator yourself?"

"Never," replied Joseph Quinlan, who has said that it is God's will that his daughter be allowed to die naturally.

"Did you ever stop to consider the fact that you couldn't do it?"

"I just couldn't do it. It wouldn't be right," Joe said. "You know, in her room, behind the bed, there's an outlet, all lined up like in a metal covering, and one part of it has been broken for three or four days. I even mentioned it to one of the nurses so she could get it fixed, because I can just see somebody . . . . Part of it sticks out and the wires are exposed like in the back of it. And I can just see somebody reach for the lamp or something and hit that wire and cause it to short. Maybe they don't have shorts in the hospital, I don't know. But I wouldn't want to see . . . ." Again, he paused for a few, painful moments, gathering his thoughts. "If this is going to be done, let it be done the right way. We'll have to be there praying for her and there'll have to be a doctor and nurse in charge just in case there's any last minute comfort we can offer her. If it's the Lord's will, He'll take her. If not, she'll go on . . . . If she could live off the machine—it has happened. It's a possibility. Not too much of a possibility."

"It's so strange," said Julie Quinlan, who testified in court that her daughter had specifically said, on several occasions when dying family friends were being discussed, that she would never want to be maintained on machines. "You know, many times when I've gone down there, the tube that goes into her throat, she's knocked it out just by moving. She's knocked it out on more than several occasions, so that at any time the Lord could have taken her. And that's why we pray, and pray, that God will show us His will . . . ."

"I've had that tube in my hands so many times," Joe said, "and I've put it back. It just comes right off sometimes, depending on how they have it twisted. It's just popped right off, and I've put it back. I've never taken it off."

While Joe and Julie Quinlan fought for seemingly endless months to have Karen's respirator turned off, they both said they would also fight to avoid having to themselves perform the physical act of switching off the machine.

"The hospitals and doctors put her on the machine in the first place," Joe said, "and it should be up to them to take her off, under supervision, with the clergy and so forth, in a private room . . . . But never, for an individual like me . . . to go in and, so-call, 'pull the plug.' I couldn't do it. That would seem altogether different to me. They're the ones who put her on the machine, they're the ones who should take her off."

"But what would you do," I asked, prior to the state Supreme Court ruling in their favor, "if it were finally decided that the respirator could be turned off, but only if you did it yourself?"

"That would be very cruel, in my opinion," Julie said, "to make the person who is nearest to the sick person do something like that. We've been through enough of an emotional and physical strain, and then to do something like that—I think that would be . . . ."

"It would be the lowest of the lows, really," Joe interrupted.

"Would you be able to do it?"

"Morally," Joe responded without hesitation.

"But maybe not physically and emotionally," I asked, cutting him off.

"I'd say only as a very, very, last resort, if I were ordered to do it by the court; morally, legally, and everything else, but only as a last resort. Because I don't believe in it. We would want our whole family there; we would want it done in a private room; we would want [to have] any comfort we could give her, and we would want to be praying for her. Because it doesn't mean it's the end of the line. People live off the machine for months and years. There are cases where people live five, ten years off the machine with brain damage. Who knows the will of God?"

"Do you really, in your heart of hearts, think she'll live off the machine?"

"Probably not," Joseph Quinlan said very softly.

During an earlier conversation, Julie Quinlan had spoken of attempting to determine God's will, of attempting to find an explanation for an inexplicable situation. "We've been praying as a family and praying so much to see God's will in this," she told me. "And there have been so many days it's been very, very difficult, when we really couldn't see any reason for it. But it is God's will and we just feel that . . ." she hesitated, . . ."I don't know how to say it. If it was God's will that she die, He could have taken her when she first went to the hospital. He could have taken her a month ago. He could take her at any time. And, as I say, we've been praying to see God's will and I feel now that He is showing us the way, that perhaps this is the reason why Karen is lasting so long—to bring this to everyone's attention and, perhaps, to have this resolved legally. And it may help other people in the same situation."

Joe Quinlan has been extremely sensitive to statements made in the press and in court to the effect that he wants to kill his daughter by turning off her respirator. Throughout our conversations he would continually return to that theme, saying on one occasion: "There's no attempt being made to really kill her. I just feel Karen's a very young girl and she's a good girl. And somewhere there's a loving God, a loving Father, just waiting for her. And there's a special place for her. And I want to get her back in her natural state and leave it up to Him to decide if he's going to take her now or later."

Part Two

THE PROBLEM

3

Whose Dignity? Whose Death?

With haste born of urgency and precision born of practice, they ran forward, half crouched, rushing the woman toward the Stanley Magic Door. As the two men guiding the rolling stretcher crossed the gray floor mat, the door swung open, admitting them to the Maryland Institute for Emergency Medicine—the Shock Trauma Unit. They followed the red line painted down the center of the corridor floor and wheeled the woman into the elevator, which stood, its doors locked open, waiting to carry them to the first floor admitting area.

The woman was technically dead before the doctors reached her side. In fact, she had ceased breathing some minutes before the helicopter carrying her to the highly sophisticated unit touched down on the parking garage roof used as a landing pad. Not only was she not breathing, but she had no pulse, for her heart had stopped beating. But in that Baltimore unit, death is often only a brief pause in the course of a life, rather than a final ending. So the fact that the woman was dead did not deter the unit's highly trained staff. They simply hooked up a full-volume respirator that began breathing for the woman. They massaged, shocked, and beat her heart, until, as though is could stand no more, it began to beat again. And, like a modern day Lazarus, the woman "rose again from the dead."

Then the surgeons rushed the woman into the adjoining operating theater an began exploratory surgery. They could repair the bones smashed in the automobile accident. They could patch the torn and mangled flesh. They could tie off the ruptured vessels and attempt to replace those which they couldn't repair. But then they came to the liver. And they stopped. For they could not replace her liver, at least not in the limited amount of time they had. And there is no artificial liver machine. So they turned off the respirator. And she died a second time.

Some would say that the doctor who turned off the respirator was playing God, that he murdered the woman, that he was obligated to sustain her life as long as the respirator could maintain her breathing and keep her blood oxygenated. But if the doctors were playing God, they were doing so when they turned the machines on. For any man can take a life, but those doctors did what we are told only God can do—they gave the woman life. Is it fair to argue that they then had an obligation to sustain that mechanical semblance of life? Didn't they more than fulfill their professional ethical, and humane duty when they made the valiant attempt to save the life of a patient who, at first glance, seemed far beyond saving?

Just 25 years ago, such questions were rarely asked, let alone answered. The respirator which could breathe for the patient had not yet come into general use in this country and had not yet replaced the cumbersome iron lung that had long been associated with the care of polio victims and other chronically ill patients. The full-volume respirator that could save the life of the trauma patient, the individual in an acute crisis, was still only a dream in most hospitals and medical centers. It wasn't until the early 1960s that the respirator became a fixture of the American medical scene, and even then its use was confined, for the most part, to big city hospitals and teaching institutions. Today, however, most large hospitals, and indeed, many smaller ones, have such devices, and their use is no more extraordinary than the use of aspirin. Medical miracles, such as bringing a woman back from the dead, have become so common as to no longer be considered miraculous. Unless the patient is famous, or infamous, or the manner of injury particularly ghastly or bizarre, we never hear of such cases. We do not hear that the life-saving machinery has been turned on, and we do not hear that it has been turned off. When the machine is turned off, there are no ethicists around to debate the morality of the act. In the quiet privacy of the operating room or intensive care unit, an assessment is made, an order given, a switch thrown. Doctors simply reason that they had activated the particular machine in order to see if they could save the patient; and, when they see that their skill and training are still insufficient, they turn off the machine. There is, they would argue, no decision to make. Such decisions to turn off life-sustaining respirators are really no different from the nondecision, made in operating rooms every day, to turn off the heart-lung machine at the conclusion of open-heart surgery. The heart-lung machine is simply used to get the patient through the operation. If the operation succeeds, the machine is turned off and the patient's heart takes over once again. If the operation fails, the machine is turned off, the heart does not beat, and the patient dies. The patient does not die because the machine is turned off. He dies because his heart does not start beating.

Thus it is with Karen Ann Quinlan, who will die not because MA1 mechanical respirator was turned off but because her brain was so badly damaged that it could not perform its natural function of regulating respiration. Had the respirator not been turned on early on the morning of April 15, 1975, Karen Ann would have been dead within days, if not minutes. But in order to assess the extent of her illness, and in order to protect her brain from further damage, the attending physicians made the only possible decision: they turned the machine on. The only difference between the case of Karen Ann Quinlan and the case of the woman in Baltimore is that you have heard of Karen Ann Quinlan; and her original physicians refused to give up. They would not acknowledge their human shortcomings and insisted on playing God. The doctors apparently did not understand the true message of their attorney, Ralph Porzio, when he argued in New Jersey Superior Court against "executing" Karen Ann, by telling Judge Robert Muir, Jr., that "there are episodes of pain and anguish and sorrow and grief in this life that neither the law or any legal system can cure . . . . In a general way . . . we are born in pain and we live in pain and unless we are very fortunate, we die in pain . . . . I think that we must recognize as a fact of life, your Honor, all of us believe that we can live in a painless society. Well, we can't . . . . We do live in a vale of tears and that is why our brief points to judicial restraint, rather than judicial intervention."

Ralph Porzio, one of the five attorneys who opposed Joe and Julia's request that they be allowed to order Karen taken off the respirator, was attempting to convince Judge Muir that the law could not relieve the Quinlan family of the anguish of watching Karen Ann living on and on as a withered appendage of a machine. But what the attorney and the lower court judge seemed to miss was that Ralph Porzio, hired and paid for by a medical malpractice insurance carrier, actually presented one of the most compelling arguments in favor of ending the medical molestation of the remains of Karen Ann Quinlan. For Mr. Porzio's argument was nothing less than a Calvinist admonition to leave to God those decisions which are God's, to recognize that there are, indeed, "episodes of pain and anguish and sorrow and grief in this life" that neither "the law or any legal system"—nor our men-made gods, physicians—can cure. We can do just so much to ease our way through this vale of tears. We must recognize our human limitations and cease our over reaching. For there comes a time when we as men must say: "Enough; there is nothing more that we can do. This situation is beyond human control."

Karen Ann Quinlan's name is one which should never have become known outside her family and circle of friends and acquaintances. For her first 21 years of life appear to have differed little from those of countless millions of other young Americans, with no accomplishment to single her out for the notoriety she achieved. And just as we should not have known of her life, so we should not have known of her dying and death. For in that too, there was little to distinguish Karen Ann Quinlan from thousands and thousands of persons who die under so-called inexplicable circumstances, which, upon closer examination, turn out to be nothing more inexplicable than stroke, heart failure, drug overdose, or as may have been the case with Karen Ann Quinlan, the untimely ingestion of alcohol and tranquilizers. The reason we came to hear of Karen Ann Quinlan is that she was not allowed to die. By a strange combination of circumstances she became a martyr of technology and the benevolence of medical science run amok. She has come to symbolize the difficulty some have in dying in this age of eternal life—an age when machines replace lungs, kidneys, and hearts; when one person's kidneys may be given to another; when the phrase "an eye for and eye" could be a slogan for the Lion's Club eye bank; and monkey brains are kept "alive" outside monkey bodies.

Joseph Quinlan did not want his daughter to die, he wanted her left in peace. He wanted, as he so often said to

anyone who would listen, "to place her in the hands of the
Lord." And thus her continuing to live for a period of time
after her removal from the respirator does not, in any way,
effect the validity of his original request, or alter the issues
involved in the case. As a reasonably intelligent, rational
human being, Joe Quinlan could see that the treatment
prescribed for his daughter—the provision of respiratory
support with a mechanical respirator—was doing nothing to
improve her condition. He saw that it was not prolonging her
life; it was only prolonging her dying. So he and his wife,
who had adopted Karen at four weeks of age, who had
nurtured, protected, and guided her through childhood and
adolescence and into young adulthood, asked her physicians
to cease their useless treatment. The Karen they knew and
loved was long dead. She died shortly after the night of April
15, 1975. All that remained of her, other than warm, vivid,
memories, was what several nationally renowned neurologists
described as a "brain stem preparation," a bundle of basic
reflexes and nerves housed in the shell of what was Karen
Ann Quinlan's body. But the physicians who had been
treating Karen would not stop treating her. They could find
no   precedent,   they   testified   in   court,   for   ending
life-sustaining treatment for a patient who still had life to
sustain. It is doubtful we will ever really know why they took
that position. The only thing we know for sure is that they
were not unaware of the legal problems facing the medical
profession in an era when malpractice has come to mean
treating unsuccessfully rather than treating improperly. We
know, for instance, that the same week the Quinlans filed
their petition in Superior Court, Dr. Arshad Javed contacted
his   malpractice   insurance   carrier,   told   them   he   was
concerned, and asked for legal assistance. The malpractice
carrier, Chubb & Son, Inc., provided Dr. Javed with the
services of Ralph Porzio. Porzio was described to me by Jesse
Benton, Chubb's vice president for claims, as "probably one

of the most distinguished legal-medical men in the state. . . . We were responsible for his bills. . . . I don't know if [a possible malpractice suit] was *their* main fear, but it was the basis on which [Javed] came to us. They must have been concerned about it."

Without a doubt, there were precedents for the action requested of the two physicians. In hospitals all over America, and, indeed, all over the world, physicians and relatives of patients daily decide to cease life-sustaining treatment in hopeless cases. These decisions to withhold or end treatment are made in cases involving severely deformed and retarded newborn infants or adults who are, for one reason or another, incapable of making decisions for themselves. And, they are made by competent adults who decide to stop fighting the inevitable and accept death. In most of these cases the physicians, patients, and relatives involved go through much the same anguish as Joe and Julie Quinlan. The decision-making process, as you will read in the following pages, is the same. The only real difference is that these other families suffer in private rather than in the public arena. And many of these unpublicized cases involve patients whose affliction is far less severe and whose outlook is far more hopeful than was Karen Ann Quinlan's. Many of these are cases where relatives and physicians are truly making value judgements, where decisions are, without a doubt, based on the "quality of life" the patient would lead if the patient were to survive.

But the Quinlan case was not such a case, as much as those who opposed Joseph Quinlan's plea tried to make it seem that was the issue being discussed. All the Quinlan case really involved was a question of when may a physician, or relatives, deem a case hopeless and end treatment of a terminally ill patient. It was not, as all involved quickly came to realize, a vehicle to redefine death. It was not a "quality of life" case. It was, in fact, no case at all. Joseph Quinlan should never have been forced to go to court, and Judge Robert Muir, Jr., should have attempted to end the matter by ruling that the questions involved were such that they should be settled by the Quinlans and Karen's physicians, without fear of civil or prosecutorial interference. Instead, Judge Muir set off a wave of confusion and near panic among those who practice emergency medicine by declaring that decisions to end life-sustaining treatment are medical decisions, but a physician who makes such a decision, and acts on it, risks being charged with murder if the patient dies. Such a dictum does not leave the profession much room for maneuvering.

Neither the Quinlans nor observers of the case held much hope that the New Jersey Supreme Court would improve at all on what Judge Muir had done. It came as a complete surprise, therefore, when the state's highest court ruled unanimously that if a physician deems a comatose patient has no chance of recovering consciousness and a hospital's board of ethics concurs in that opinion, then the physician may withdraw the life support systems. The court also clearly spelled out the right of the patient's relatives to seek a new physician and transfer the patient to another hospital, as the Quinlans did, if the original physician and hospital would not comply with their wishes. In addition, the court held that no one involved in such a case could be held civilly or criminally liable. What the court did, in effect, was sanction current medical practice. It made public and licit a decision-making process which has hitherto been largely secret and technically illicit, if indeed not illegal. "We glean from the record here that physicians distinguish between curing the ill and comforting and easing the dying" wrote Chief Justice and former Governor of New Jersey Richard J. Hughes, "that they refuse to treat the curable as if they were dying or ought to die, and that they had sometimes refused to treat the hopeless and dying as if they are curable."

Justice Hughes then made note that several physicians

had testified during the trial in the lower court that they had "refused to inflict an undesired prolongation of the process of dying on a patient in irreversible condition when it is clear that such 'therapy' offers neither human or humane benefit . . . . We think these attitudes represent a balanced implementation of a profoundly realistic perspective on the meaning of life and death and that they respect the whole Judeo-Christian tradition of regard for human life. No less would they seem consistent with the moral matrix of medicine, 'to heal,' very much in the sense of the endless mission of the law, 'to do justice.' "

There are many who view the Quinlan case as a euthanasia case and who consider the withdrawal of life-sustaining treatment "passive euthanasia." But the case had nothing to do with euthanasia other than to cause much public discussion of the subject. And there is no such thing as "passive euthanasia." The case of Karen Ann Quinlan had nothing to do with euthanasia, because no one ever proposed doing anything to Karen Ann to hasten the natural dying process which had already begun. While the word euthanasia may literally translate "good death," it has come to be synonymous with the term "mercy killing." To mention the former is to raise the specter of the latter. To those who speak of passive euthanasia, who say that it is what the Quinlans were advocating, it must be pointed out that there is nothing passive about turning off a respirator which is sustaining a life, however "meaningless" that life may be. To begin with, one is making an active, conscious choice between two courses of action: continuing extraordinary, involved, specialized care and support and ordering that support end with the certain knowledge that ending the support will allow the death of the patient. There is certainly nothing passive about that, and to call such action passive is not only to do violence to the language but also to refuse to accept the consequence of an action by calling it inaction.

Labeling the cessation of treatment in a hopeless case euthanasia or mercy killing is also an injustice. For no one is killing the patient. No one is, in reality, doing anything to hasten the patient's death. What one is doing is allowing a natural, irreversible process, namely death, to continue its course. No one suggested injecting air into Karen Quinlan's veins. No one wished to give her poison. No one placed a pillow over her head to prevent her lungs from taking in oxygen. Instead the physicians who took over her treatment acknowledged that they could not further help her. They decided that the treatment being given her had not helped Karen and was harming those who loved her. So just as they would stop prescribing an antibiotic for a patient for whom the antibiotic proved worthless, they said they would not again turn on a respirator, a piece of life-sustaining equipment that had not helped Karen Ann Quinlan. Of course, Karen Ann Quinlan eventually will die. But she will not be killed by the physicians; she will be killed by disease. Such a practice is not euthanasia. It is simply sound medicine.

There are those who fear the Quinlan decision will provide physicians and relatives with the legal rationale for the medical execution of retarded children, rich or poor elderly parents, and other relatives. But the decision does no such thing. In the first place, the decision only applies to cases in which the patient is comatose and doctors hold that there is no hope the patient will ever recover to a "cognitive, sapient state." In using those words the court was not applying a "quality of life" criteria but rather was using the terms, as they were used during the trial of the case, to refer to a person having *any* responsiveness or awareness at all. In other words, were there any hope whatsoever that Karen Ann Quinlan could ever improve at all, even to the level of a newborn infant, the respirator could *not* have been turned off. In addition, the decision indirectly provides protection for the retarded, aged, and social misfits on whom family members or a society run amok might practice euthanasia by sanctioning, and thereby making public, current medical practices. The case and decision have set off endless discussions and debates not only on withholding care but also on euthanasia, mercy killing. It is helping to make the general public aware of what is going on in hospital intensive care units and the back rooms to which the dying are relegated. Ever since the Quinlan case was filed in court in September 1975, the wire services have been carrying stories from all over the country about patients in comas, patients who have recovered from comas, patients whose life support systems were turned off, and relatives of comatose patients who requested that life support systems be turned off. Those same things were happening every day prior to Joseph Quinlan's filing his extraordinary plea, but they were not aired publically. Now they are.

In any concurrent discussion of the Quinlan case and euthanasia, it is useful to keep in mind the Roman Catholic Church's position on Joseph Quinlan's request and the Supreme Court decision: the Church, through the Bishop of the Paterson, New Jersey, Diocese, supported the decision of the Quinlan family and the high court. The Catholic Church is, and always has been, violently opposed to any form of euthanasia. But at the same time, the Church has for centuries sanctioned withholding useless treatments in hopeless cases. According to Father John Connery, S.J., of the Kennedy Institute for the Study of Human Reproduction and Bioethics at Georgetown University, the Church's position can be traced back to the Renaissance. When a person was condemned to burn at the stake, Father Connery explained, he was offered a single bucket of water to cool himself while burning. It was not obligatory to use that one bucket, for it would only prolong the agony, rather than saving the individual. By the same token, a person

condemned to starve to death was not considered morally
obligated to eat his last meal, for eating that meal would only
postpone the inevitable.

Prior to the development of anesthesia, the position of
the Church had been refined to take into account the moral
obligation to use "extraordinary," versus "ordinary," means
to save a life. In the days when the removal of a limb was as
life threatening and painful an ordeal as leaving on a diseased
limb, it was considered "extraordinary," and therefore not
obligatory, to undergo surgery—even if avoiding surgery
meant certain death. And in 1957, Pope Pius XII told a group
of anesthesiologists that neither they nor their patients were
morally obligated to use such modern devices as respirators
to maintain life where there was no hope for recovery. While
the use of the terms "ordinary" and "extraordinary" can lead
to protracted debates about which medical device, drug, or
technique is which, it is really quite simple to distinguish
between the ordinary and the extraordinary. If the use of a
device or treatment csrries with it the reasonable hope or
expectation that it will improve the patient's condition, and
its use will not impose an overwhelming burden, such as
bankruptcy or horrible pain, upon the patient or family
members, its use is considered ordinary. Thus, the use of a
respirator would be considered ordinary to sustain a patient
through a severe bout with a respiratory disease. If, however,
the treatment or device will not help or would impose an
overwhelming burden on the patient, its use is considered
extraordinary. As Father Connery was prepared to testify at
the Quinlan trial, the use of the respirator would be
considered extraordinary to maintain a patient like Karen
Ann. In fact, the use of antibiotics, and even high calorie
food, could be considered extraordinary in her case.

It may seem paradoxical that a church which is known
for its opposition to birth control, abortion and euthanasia,
and for its belief in the absolute sanctity of human life,

would be so seemingly liberal on the question of ceasing treatment in hopeless cases. If one examines these apparently opposite positions, however, in light of the Church's foundation in Roman, rather than Anglo-Saxon, law, one realizes that there is nothing at all contradictory. For Roman law, unlike Anglo-Saxon law, consists of a series of general principles or guidelines—all human life is sacred and to be protected—to which there are numerous, often granted, exceptions. Anglo-Saxon law, on the other hand, is made up of specific rules to which there are no exceptions granted for anyone. While lay Catholics are all aware of the general principles upon which the Church is founded, very few are aware of all the exceptions to those principles. Many of the exceptions, including that concerning the use of extraordinary means to maintain life in hopeless cases, make up what has historically been referred to as the "discipline of the secret." These "secrets" are known to the clergy, and are told to individual lay members of the Church as they have a need to known them. Thus Father Trapasso, the Quinlans' parish priest, told them of the Church position on withholding care.

The Quinlan case and its attendant publicity has terrified many conservative Catholics because what was a secret (to be discovered only as the need to know it arose) is now known to anyone who reads newspapers or watches television. These conservatives fear that, in a nation founded on the principles of Anglo-Saxon law, the laity will view the position on withholding care as a law, to which there are no exceptions, rather than as a special application of a general principle. What then, the conservatives wonder, of the Church's position on abortion and euthanasia?

The Quinlans were made aware of all these problems by James Crowley, an attorney and close friend of Paul Armstrong, who assisted Armstrong in the preparation of the case. For although he did not make the fact public, James Crowley is a former seminarian who, in addition to religious

training in America, spent five years studying at the Roman
Major Seminary at the Lateran in Rome. Had he chosen to
remain until ordination, Crowley would most likely have
entered the Vatican diplomatic corps. Because of his Church
background and his contacts in the American Catholic
hierarchy, Crowley was able to assure Church officials that
the Quinlans and their attorneys were, indeed, adhering to
orthodox Catholic policy, and he was able to evaluate the
various Church statements on the case, knowing, as he did,
the status of those who issued the statements and for whom
they were issuing them.

It is unfortunate, in some ways, that money never
became an issue in the Quinlan case. It is, of course,
fortunate for Joseph and Julia Quinlan that Karen Ann was
an adult, and technically an indigent one at that, and they
thus escaped the staggering debt with which they would have
been burdened had they been responsible for her care.
Instead, we are all paying Karen's bills through our Social
Security withholding taxes, bills in excess of $160,000. Had
the Quinlans been forced to pay for Karen's treatment, the
financial question might have been discussed in detail. We
would have been forced to come to grips with the question of
whether our limited health care resources should be used to
maintain a "brain stem preparation," when open heart
surgery could be provided for infants or children for whom
such surgery would offer a chance for a normal life. Or
whether the money should be used to turn our mental
institutions from disgraceful holding pens into hospitals that
provide training and rehabilitation. Obviously, if there is any
hope for Karen's recovery, there should not be any question
of sparing expense. It would be here that the application of
the "meaningful life" concept becomes valid: If there is any
chance that a patient can lead a life which will be meaningful
to the patient—and one must assume that even a severley
retarded individual, as long as he has any degree of

self-awareness, can lead a life meaningful to himself—one is obligated to do all one can to save the patient. But there was never any thought that Karen Ann Quinlan would recover, would ever again possess any of those qualities which distinguish us as human beings. She would never again see, hear, feel, touch, have any awareness of her surroundings or be able to respond in any way to other human beings, even as a newborn responds. Is this, then, the patient on whom our limited health dollars should be spent?

Yet another concept discussed both inside and outside the courtroom in the wake of the Quinlan case is that of "death with dignity," a term which has come to encompass everything from dying at home in one's own bed to out and out euthanasia by giving a suffering patient an overdose of pain killer to enable him to die pain free, "with dignity." The first questions to be considered are: Whose dignity? Whose death? Too often, talk of death with dignity comes from the relatives of the dying or from social scientists and philosophers who consider the sight of the dying somewhat undignified. They are primarily referring to the patient who lies in a hospital bed, tubes protruding from his or her arms and attached to machines of various sorts. But what is so inherently undignified about being fed intravenously or having one's respiration aided by a mechanical device? Dignity is something one either does or does not possess. It is an inherent, personal, indefinable concept. If a person lives with dignity, a person dies with dignity. If a person does not live with dignity, a person will not die with dignity. A dying patient in a hospital may be sustained by the steady drip from a glucose bottle but still feel as dignified as she felt when she was healthy. Her relatives, on the other hand, may consider the scene distasteful and unseemly and thereby rob the patient of her sense of self-worth.

I remember visiting a cancer patient, a woman in her early sixties who was living at home with her family. She had

had most of her cancerous lower jaw and tongue removed; and her rebuilt jaw, feeding tube, and metal respirator fitting can only be described as grotesque. The woman couldn't talk but communicated with a writing pad she carried about the house with her. Yes, although she was dying of cancer she was able to be up and about with her family. How horrifying, I thought, to live like that. How "undignified." But "undignified" for whom? For me, because I was initially repulsed by the woman's ugliness? Or for the woman, who was, after all, alive and functioning, surrounded by her children and grandchildren, all of whom did their part to take care of her?

None of this is to suggest that hospitals are good places to die or that it is pleasant to have one's veins jammed with needles and tubes. It does, however, suggest that our efforts are misplaced when we spend our time debating the merits of "death with dignity." What we should be doing instead is educating ourselves to the fact that, as the New Jersey Supreme Court ruled, a dying patient has a right to refuse useless treatment. "We have no doubt," wrote Chief Justice Hughes, "in these unhappy circumstances, that if Karen herself were miracuously lucid for an interval (not altering the prognosis of the condition to which she would soon return) and perspective of her irreversible condition, she could effectively decide upon the discontinuance of the life-support apparatus, even if it meant the prospect of natural death. . . . We have no hesitancy in deciding. . . that no external compelling interest of the state could compel Karen to endure the unendurable, only to vegetate a few measurable months with no realistic possibility of returning to a cognitive or sapient life. We perceive no thread of logic distinguishing between such a choice on Karen's part and a similar choice which, under the evidence in this case, could be made by a competent patient terminally ill, riddled by cancer and suffering great pain; such a patient would not be resuscitated or put on a respirator "according to the testimony of several physicians' and *a fortiori* would not be kept *against his will* on a respirator." The question, then becomes one of an individual's being allowed to die at all, not of his or her being allowed to die with dignity. Joseph Quinlan repeatedly spoke of Karen's being allowed to die with "grace and dignity." Karen will not die with "grace and dignity," for there is nothing graceful about her 70-pound living corpse, and brain stem preparations do not possess "dignity." What Joseph Quinlan was really discussing was his own dignity and that of his family. "Do not continue to subject us to this horror, this indignity of watching the decay of what is left of the young woman we loved. Allow us to bury our dead in peace."

Attorney Paul Armstrong, in his closing argument, put the issue in its proper perspective when he said: "In determining Karen's moral best interest we ask the court to take into account the complex of values and attitudes which recognize and give meaning to the term, dignity of man. At present, Karen lies in St. Clare's Hospital, no more than 60 or 70 pounds of flesh and bone; a poor and tragic creature whose life is no more than a patterned series of the most primitave nervous reflexes, while in this courtroom is seriously proposed, in the face of the most compelling contrary medical testimony, that her now disunified and unperceiving body be constrained to functioned against all its natural impulses.

"Could anything be more degrading to a human being— a human being who has come on this earth full of love and promise, and who has known peace and joy, who has been the daughter of Joseph and Julia Quinlan? Can anything be more degrading than to be offered up as a living sacrifice to the materialistic and misguided belief that death can be somehow cheated, if only we find the right combination of wires and gauges, transistors and tubes?"

Part Three

THE SAVIORS AND THE SAVED

4

. . . We'll Keep the Electrons Snapping

"My imagination, unbidden, possessed and guided me, gifting the successive images that arose in my mind with a vividness far beyond the usual bounds of reverie. I saw—with shut eyes, but acute mental vision—I saw the thing he has put together. I saw the hideous phantasm of a man stretched out, and then, on the working of some powerful engine, show signs of motion. Frightful must it be, for supremely frightful would be the effect of any human endeavour to mock the stupendous mechanism of the Creator of the world. His success would terrify the artist; he would rush away from his odious handiwork, horror-striken. He would hope that, left to itself, the slight spark of life which he had communicated would fade, that animation would subside into dead matter, and he might sleep in the belief that the silence of the grave would quench forever the transient existence of the hideous corpse which he had looked upon as the cradle of life. . . . "

Mary Wollstonecraft Shelley, explaining in the introduction to Frankenstein, *how she came to write that book, in 1818.*

"We don't have much equipment to work with—you give us a couple of cells and we'll keep the electrons snapping. But it may be that if you remove the one-to-one nursing, and the attention to position, when the system swings out of balance, it won't swing back. It's not neglect: It's just that the support isn't there. You don't have to yank the I.V.s. . ."

From an interview with the director of the intensive care unit of a major Eastern medical center, 1974.

Victor Frankenstein, who should not be confused with his monster, is alive and well, now practictng medicine 158 years after his creation. He is still bringing the dead back to life, and he continues to take organs and parts from one body to implant in, and graft onto, another. He uses jolts of electricity to restart stilled hearts, although he does not have to use thunderstorms to perform *that* miracle as he did in the movie version of his fictional life. His laboratory and operating theater are still filled with humming, buzzing pieces of exotic equipment and jars and vials of blood and other fluids. But in 1818 Frankenstein and his monster were only figments of Mrs. Shelley's vivid and prophetic imagination—she did, after all, describe the Baron's work 101 years before the first successful use of an injection to restart a nonfunctioning human heart, 110 years before the discovery of penicillin, and 132 years before the first successful human kidney transplant. Today, however, there are thousands of Victor Frankensteins, and they are very real. They are the physicians to whom we give the battered corpses scraped off our highways and the bloodied victims of urban carnage—physicians who usually give us in return not monsters but our friends and relatives made whole once again.

The physician who has at his disposal a modern, well-equipped emergency room, operating room, and intensive care unit can perform medical miracles beyond even Mrs. Shelley's wildest dream. Not only can he transplant or arrange for the transplantation of a variety of vital organs, not only can he restart a dead heart, but he can also perform many miracles—remove and replace a patient's blood; cool the blood to slow the circulation during surgery; replace the patient's respiratory function with a machine; temporarily replace the patient's heart and circulatory system with a machine; replace burned or damaged skin; rebuild mangled features; and even replace damaged joints. Like Victor Frankenstein, these physicians have only the best of intentions. But also like Victor Frankenstein, they sometimes create monsters. Theirs are not the sort of Late Show monsters who run amok, killing children and terrifying villagers. But they are, nevertheless, monsters who by their very existence destroy families and ruin lives. They are persons whose minds and bodies have been so massively, irrevocably damaged that neither they nor their families know who they are. They are alive only in a technical sense. They are the Karen Ann Quinlans who lie in intensive care units and nursing homes all across America.

Because of the advances in emergency medicine in the past two decades, the development of technology that has made it possible to save the formerly unsavable, it is inevitable that some monsters be created. Unless physicians begin to decide whom to treat and whom to shun at the point of their initial encounter, they are bound to make some mistakes. Obviously, in times of war or mass disaster, through a process known as triage, physicians make such choices, for they have limited resources that must be allocated to those who can best benefit from them. But under normal circumstances, there is no way to rationalize making such truly Godlike choices. The physician must go all out for every patient, even for example, for a patient like Karen Ann Quinlan.

The "couple of cells" the intensive care director spoke of hypothetically were still there when the Lakeland Rescue Squad ambulance pulled up to the entrance of Newton

Memorial Hospital early on the morning of April 15, 1975. In retrospect, however, it seems likely there was little else left of the person called Karen Ann Quinlan. The police reported that when they arrived at the house at which Karen was staying she was blue and pulseless. She had been in that condition, they reported, for at least 15 minutes, and possibly for as long as one half hour. When the ambulance crew arrived and began to administer oxygen to Karen, her color began to return, but there is little doubt her brain was already damaged. Hospital records indicate that Karen had difficulty breathing during the first half hour after her admission to Newton Memorial, and the decision was made to put her on a respirator to aid her breathing. There was little else the attending physicians could do or should have done. They did not know Karen's medical history. They did not have an accurate idea of how long her brain had been deprived of oxygen—the brain may suffer damage after only three minutes of oxygen deprivation, but it was impossible to tell how much oxygen her brain had, or had not, gotten. And the physicians did not know what caused her respiratory difficulties. Looking at the records months later, and knowing that Karen had been drinking and had taken some tranquilizers, it is possible to speculate that she might have passed out, vomited, and choked on her own vomit. That theory is strengthened by the fact that within two days she had developed pneumonia in both her lungs. We can only guess why no one ever noticed any vomit, but it might have been forced back down her trachea during attempts to revive her. But that is all conjecture. All the attending physicians knew was that they were treating a comatose young woman, possibly the victim of a drug overdose, whom they assumed at the time they could save. Had they assumed otherwise, they would have been unforgivably derelict in their duties as physicians.

But in saving Karen Ann Quinlan, a group of well-meaning physicians created a modern Frankenstein's monster. For they took the near lifeless body of a young woman and, rather than leaving her to herself in order that "the slight spark of life which [they] had communicated would fade, that this thing which had received such imperfect animation would subside into dead matter," they fought to keep Karen Ann alive until she could be transferred to St. Clare's Hospital, where yet another team of doctors worked against all odds and the wishes of the Quinlan family for more than a year. And what they worked so hard to save was a monster, which the Oxford English Dictionary defines variously as "something extraordinary or unnatural," and "an animal or plant deviating in one or more of its parts from the normal type . . . ." And how else can one categorize a full grown woman, shrunk to 70 pounds, comatose for more than a year, her joints totally frozen by calcification, her breathing maintained by a machine, her teeth grinding together and gnawing through her lower lip?

Once such a monster has been created, the creator has three legally permissible options. The first is that decided on by Karen's attending physicians: Go all out to maintain the life of the patient, despite the fact that "heroic" effort is of no benefit to the patient, the patient's family, the physicians themselves, or society in general. Such an option involves avoiding the question of who is being denied a bed in the intensive care unit while that bed is occupied for more than a year by a patient who is not benefiting from the facilities.

The second option is one much more commonly chosen, and that is for the director of the intensive care unit to conclude that the patient is no longer benefiting from the care of the unit and to order his or her removal to another area of the hospital. This is the option suggested in the second of two quotes with which I began this chapter.

"Remove the one-to-one nursing and attention to position, when the system swings out of balance, it won't swing back," and the patient will die. But that position is clearly a cop out, and the physician who takes it is ducking his professional responsibilities. He is refusing to let "the slight spark of life fade" and is forcing someone else, another physician, or, as is usually the case, a nurse, to oversee the death of a patient. The physician I quoted at the beginning of the chapter, who quite understandably did not want his name associated with his views, also told me that if brain damage has left a person speechless and essentially unresponsive and his vital functions are beautiful but he cannot control his bowels, can't turn, can't function, "we have fulfilled our responsibility for this patient. You brought him to us for life support. Now its up to rehabilitation. Our mission is to get enough life support hauled back together and stable so that another means of care can be instituted outside the unit."

Then there is the third option, and that is for the physician to accept full responsibility for the care of the patient, including deciding to end care when that care is no longer of benefit to the patient. There are many physicians willing to accept that awesome responsibility, but few who are willing to admit publically that they do so. But some, like Dr. Jack Zimmerman, director of the intensive care unit at George Washington University Medical Center, are perfectly frank in discussing their work. "All the intensive care unit is," Dr. Zimmerman told me, shortly after Judge Muir's decision, "is an area where various technologies can be utilized best to support somebody through an acute reversible crisis. And unfortunately, that definition of reversible can't be made at the doorstep. More often than not it can't be made. So one errs on the side of using that technology until one defines irreversible, or perhaps some technical infeasibility which is the same thing."

"I take it there would have been no problem here in turning off Karen Quinlan's respirator. That her parents would have said, 'the time has come,' and you would have agreed," I asked Dr. Zimmerman, shortly after Judge Muir had ruled that such an action would constitute a homocide.

"Yes. That would have transpired in our unit. The family's wishes would have been met."

"How long would you have kept going before you would have given up on her, based on what you've read about the case?"

"It would have been quite some time, because of her youth, because there were drugs involved and because of our ability to evaluate the nervous system [when it] is thrown off by drugs. So in her situation, we would err on the side of creating a vegetable because we just could not predict [the outcome] from any of our studies," said Dr. Zimmerman. "And in our unit it would have come out exactly the same way as any long term intensive care unit admission; seeking a state of stability, supporting as necessary, until we could define what we had. And it would have taken quite some time because of the extraneous things like drugs."

"But would it have taken you as long as it seemed to be taking in St. Clare's?"

"It would have been unusual for it to have taken that long in our unit. I think that it would vary with who the attending physician was. But with any patient who's in the unit that long, I've established a coincidental relationship with the family, and I think the subject [of ending care and turning off the respirator] would have been approached if the family hadn't approached it much sooner," said Dr. Zimmerman.

The George Washington intensive care unit, like the vast majority of such units around the country, takes patients from all areas of the hospital, many of whom simply need

careful monitoring for a short period following surgery or
during recovery from an illness. But at the Maryland Institute
for Emergency Medicine, commonly referred to as the Shock
Trauma Unit, there are no patients who are simply recovering
from disease or surgery. For that unit is the central feature of
a state wide emergency medicine system. The most battered
victims of trauma and violence from all over Maryland and
contiguous areas of Delaware, West Virginia, and the District
of Columbia are brought to the unit, most often by
Maryland State Police Medevac helicopter. The patients are
usually brought there for the simple reason that they stand
very little chance to survive elsewhere. And because the unit
does care only for the dead or near dead, its staff is often
faced with having to decide when to cease treatment of
patients, many of whom are in far better shape than Karen
Ann Quinlan. In fact, officials of the unit told me in 1974
that is was their policy to turn off respirators sustaining the
life of quadrapalegics, patients completely paralyzed from
the base of the skull down but patients who were, none the
less, able to see, hear, think, and (but for the respirator tubes
protruding from their throats) speak. These doctors
rationalize that such patients can never live off the respirator,
can never function for themselves in any way, are devoid of
such basic reflexes as that involved in swallowing, and will
almost inevitably succumb to infection and die within a few
months of discharge from the unit. So rather than pass the
buck to the patient's family, or a nursing home, the
physicians in the unit allow the patient to die there. Because
the unit treats such severely injured patients, because its
ability to sustain life is unparalled, and because its physicians
make such momentous decisions on a regular basis, the Shock
Trauma Unit and its work are worth an extended
examination.

□

It was 5:38 on an early spring afternoon. Dr. Ernest Hippolito was running down a corridor beside a swiftly rolling stretcher, his hospital gown flapping about his legs as he administered oxygen to the young man on the stretcher. Admitting nurse Peggy Palmer rode astride the badly mangled young man, rhythmically and repeatedly throwing all her weight onto his chest. As the stretcher was wheeled into the admitting area of the Shock Trauma Unit, the doctor and nurse shed the outer gowns they were wearing during the ambulance ride and run from the helicopter pad. And by 5:40, blood was spattering the floor as the patient was transferred to a table in the admitting area. A physician's assistant cut off what was left of the patient's clothing, as nurses unwrapped the packages of sterile instruments—always in readiness—which would be used in the attempt to save the young man. Unlike the usual emergency room, there were no patients sitting or waiting for attention. There were no beds or cubicles taken up with victims of sprains and cuts. Instead, the admission area was empty and ready. White sheets covered the four admitting table/beds. Nineteen bottles of plasma—more than are used in some major medical centers in two normal days—were hanging from stands, with needles and lines attached, ready for use. Monitors to follow the patient's blood flow and heart beat were turned on and ready to be hooked up, as they are 24 hours a day. There is never a second's hesitation to make sure the monitor is functioning once the patient is admitted. That is always taken care of beforehand.

Like all patients admitted to the Shock Trauma Unit, the young man was immediately hooked up to a full-volume respirator. Rather than wait to discover later that the patient is having respiratory problems, doctors in the unit believe in using the machine to take over the patient's breathing, allowing his system to rest, saving strength for areas where it is needed. If in the first 24 hours it is found that the patient can breathe normally without the machine, it can be turned off as easily as it was turned on. The leads from the monitors were attached to the young man's body. Peggy Palmer, who was watching the monitor, reported, "you're getting a flat line." The youth's heart was not beating. Miss Palmer paused only long enough to see that there was no variation in the monitor's signal and returned immediately to administering an external heart massage. Her hospital-issue pink pants and top were already covered with abstract patterns of swiftly drying blood.

Seventeen minutes earlier, the young man had been lying by the roadside, 36 miles north east of Baltimore, following an accident in which his car was crushed by a tractor trailer. When the Medevac helicopter reached the scene, he was in profound shock, coma, had no pulse or blood pressure. A state police medic gave the young man external heart massage and positive pressure ventilation, which involves forcing oxygen into the lungs, and continued to do so during the 12-minute flight to Baltimore. When the chopper landed on the roof of a parking garage used as a landing pad for the Shock Trauma Unit, a unit team—consisting of Dr. Hippolito (an anesthesiologist), Peggy Palmer, and a physician's assistant—was already waiting on the roof, having been alerted by radio that the patient was on the way. Before even placing the man in the waiting ambulance, the team inserted an endotracheal tube to provide a better air passage, and the team then rode with the patient during the five-minute ride through the parking garage and down the block to the rear entrance of University Hospital where the unit is located.

In almost any other facility, the young man, whose injuries included severe open depressed skull fractures with bleeding from both ears, fractures of the jaw, left arm, left leg, internal chest and abdominal bleeding, would be pronounced D.O.A. (dead on arrival). But not in the Shock

Trauma Unit. Instead, a team of surgeons, nurses, anesthesiologists, and physicians' assistants worked on the patient as though he could be revived. A surgical resident made an incision in the young man's groin and in two other parts of his body and massive quantities of blood were pumped into him. Another surgeon had already begun a procedure called abdominal lavage, or a "belly tap," which involves pumping a saline solution into the patient's abdominal cavity and draining the solution back out. If the solution turns pink, the patient is bleeding internally. The solution turned pink. But still the team worked on. Not until the line on the heart monitor had remained flat for 15 minutes did one of the nurses walk over to an intercom in the wall, push the talk button and say: "Upstairs? 5:55, know what I mean?"

"O.K.," replied the clerk in the fourth floor, critical care unit, who knows she was being told the patient died officially at 5:55 P.M. Neither the nurse nor the clerk needed to say more about the death other than for the nurse to add, "we'll get you a name in a minute." Up to that point no one knew who they were treating. Unlike most hospital emergency rooms, no questions had been asked about insurance before treatment began. There were no questions about occupation or residence, mother's maiden name, or father's social security number. No interrogation about whether the patient could pay the bill, which could run well in excess of $600 a day. The patient was simply assigned the name of John Doe and a number to distinguish him from the other John Does of the day. The questions come later.

Death in the Shock Trauma Unit is a common enough occurrence, but success, rather than failure, is the rule. According to Dr. William Gill who was clinical director of the institution at the time of the young man's admission, 83 percent of all persons picked up by the state police helicopters survive, "and that statistic includes the D.O.A.s,"

Dr. Gill said. Those who are already dead when they are picked up are still transported to the unit, he explained, because the state trooper medics do not have the authority to pronounce a person dead. "You can only guess," continued the Scottish trained general surgeon and traumatologist, "but I would think that in an ordinary emergency room, half our survivors would not survive." The reason for that, Gill told me, is that the usual hospital "lacks a dedicated area. If you have a delay for any reason, even to find an empty operating room, you've had it. It is not the gadgetry, it's having enough people and having them around the clock and having senior people." And every day and night of the week the unit is fully staffed by at least one team that is made up of a senior general surgeon, a general surgery resident, an anesthesiologist, a neurosurgery resident, several physicians' assistants, X-ray technicians, an admitting nurse, and several operating room nurses. There are also about half a dozen nurses in the fourth floor critical care area, where the patients are kept following their admission and surgery. "We can have two more teams in 15 minutes," Dr. Gill said, "and we have one senior staff man on call each week. We rarely do telephone consultations. If there's any question, we come in."

In addition to its own staff, the unit calls on the specialists from the University Hospital, who are usually no more than 10 minutes from the unit. These specialists include neurosurgeons, orthopedic surgeons, heart surgeons, thoracic surgeons, and plastic surgeons. The Shock Trauma Unit also has its own small blood bank, X-ray department, laboratory for processing test results 24 hours a day, and two operating rooms immediately adjacent to the admitting area. "When I came here in 1972," Dr. Gill said, "we didn't have our own operating rooms. We used the hospital operating rooms. In an eight-month period 15 patients died as they were wheeled the equivalent of three blocks through the hospital. That got things moving" and the unit got its own operating rooms. Although such features as being able to read the results of a blood test 15 minutes after the test is administered may not sound important, they are. As Shock Trauma Nurse Rosie Pascale told me, "working in a regular emergency room [in another hospital], I've seen patients die waiting for test results."

The Maryland Institute of Emergency Medicine, which many call the most sophisticated such facility in the United States, was established in 1961 by Dr. R. Adams Cowley as a two-bed research facility. The unit's primary goal was then, and is now, study of the effects of shock—that body state caused by rapid loss of blood or oxygen to the organs—and trauma—any severe physical injury—on the human system. But the state funded institute has grown from its miniscule beginnings into a minihospital within University Hospital, complete with two admitting areas, the two operating rooms that contain the tools of virtually every surgical trade, a 12-bed critical care area, a 14-bed intensive care area like that in most urban hospitals, a smaller recovery area and research labs, all of which are used to care for 1,000 to 1,200 patients a year. Such facilities and such care do not come cheap. The patients may be billed more than $600 a day for their stay in the critical care area, and some patients have been billed as much as $20,000 to $30,000 for stays of about 60 days. But an inability to pay such staggering bills does not make a patient ineligible for the unit's care. If the patient cannot pay, the state will.

While the unit handles a large number of patients during the course of a year, the work comes in spurts. Weeks may go by with only a half dozen admissions, and then in a single 12-hour period, 15 patients may be flown in. During one such weekend in the spring of 1975, things became so chaotic that desks were being used as beds in the admitting area, and a broken elevator necessitated carrying patients on stretchers up a flight of stairs. But it is the quiet nights that are the rule, rather than the exception—nights of joking and checking vital signs, sterilizing instruments and reorganizing supply closets, drinking coffee, and studying medical textbooks.

□

The overhead ceiling lights were dimmed in the fourth floor critical care area, and the green and red monitor lights glow in the semidark like stars in a mechanical galaxy. It was almost 1:00 A.M., and two clerks checking paper work sat on the raised observation platform that dominates the large room. The platform, which resembles the bridge of a ship, contains monitors which can read the vital signs of patients in any of the room's 12 cubicles. The monitors also feature alarms that can be set to go off if, for instance, a patient's blood pressure goes above or below a certain point. Then, however, the monitors were still. Only eight of the beds were occupied, and three nurses were working in cubicles, attempting to make patients more comfortable. In a fourth cubicle, nurse Sue Hannan readied a bed for a patient who had been in surgery since 8:30 that evening. She talked with a nurse in the next cubicle as she turned on and adjusted the monitors, preparing them so they can be attached to the patient as soon as he is wheeled into the area. Lab technician Louis Solomon, who was taking a break, sat on the steps leading up to the central platform, gazing around the unit. "It's just like in the army," he said, waving an arm from left to right, "except instead of having shell trauma here you have 70-mile-per-hour trauma. They're going to have these units all over the country."

Two and one-half hours passed quietly. Mrs. Hannan and a physician's assistant had moved the empty bed in cubicle number four down to the first floor operating room, ready to receive the patient in surgery as soon as he came off the table. There was no double transfer, from table to stretcher to bed. Just one move and then a ride through a hallway and up in the elevator. And at 3:30 A.M. the man, who less than 12 hours earlier fell out of a tree and ruptured his spleen, fractured his pelvis, fractured his left ankle and upper femur, and suffered internal damage around his bladder, was wheeled into the critical care area. He was already receiving blood from the bottle hanging from a stand on the bed frame. The monitor lines were attached to his body, and the machines were adjusted again. The bedside respirator was attached to the tube protruding from his mouth. The man was beginning to come out of the anesthesia and swiped weekly at the tube in his mouth. "You can't take it out," Dr. Hippolito told him softly but firmly. "That's your life line." The patient continued to knock at the tube, and Mrs. Hannan wrapped his hands in gauze and carefully tied them to the bed rails.

Louis Solomon, the lab technician, was watching the scene, as he told me he was taking courses and trying to get into medical school. "I watch the nurses because they know more than any second-year medical student. You know, you see a lot of crud up here." He pauses. "But somebody has to deal with it."

It was 4:06 A.M. The patient in bed four gestured and tried unsuccessfully to move a hand toward his respirator tube. Mrs. Hannan, who was in the midst of laughing at another nurse's joke, froze in mid-laugh and became immediately solicitous. "Does it hurt," she asked the man. He attempted to nod. "I know honey. I'll get you some morphine." The words were not only words, they were an auditory caress. "Does your tube bother you?" The patient again nodded. "The doctor'll be up early in the morning," Mrs. Hannan told the man. "They'll take it out then." He looked a bit relieved. At least someone was telling him something.

It was 4:30 A.M. In the tiny lounge off the operating rooms on the first floor a group of operating and admission

personnel were discussing the television program M.A.S.H.
The conversation moved from the television show to work in
the unit, which is, after all, virtually the same thing. "The big
thing that has struck me about this place, especially when I'm
out driving," one of the nurses said, "is how your chances
vary depending upon where you're taken afterwards."
Another nurse mentioned a friend who has a mororcycle, and
a debate was on. For drunks and motorcycles are two of the
touchiest subjects in the lounge. Everyone has his or her
drunken driver or mangled-motorcycle-rider story, like the
one about the man whose car rammed another head on,
killing several persons, who was uninjured himself and was so
drunk he didn't know where or who he was, or another story
about a motorcycle rider who came to the unit as a transfer
patient from another hospital, with his leg torn off and
jammed under his arm. "I love motorcycles," said nurse
Virginia Day. "But once I started working here . . . I see one
and I say, 'fool, you're going to see me in Shock Trauma.' "

□

The majority of the patients admitted to the unit are
the victims of auto accidents, and half of those, Dr. Gill told
me, have alcohol in their blood. About one quarter of those
patients are legally drunk. Just as the subject of drunken
drivers sets off some of the nurses, so a discussion of medical
politics sets Dr. Gill on edge. All the full-time men are general
surgeons," he said. "We feel there should be a class of
surgeons called traumatologists who can perform any type of
surgery in a life-saving situation. Twenty-five years ago it was
decided there should be a board specialty in trauma. But
because nobody could decide on who would be the parent
board—the general surgeons, the orthopedic surgeons, the
cardiac surgeons—nothing's been done . . . . It used to be
insisted that we didn't even put tubes in the chest unless we

were thoracic surgeons," Dr. Gill said. "It's improving. But professional feuding is a big problem—it's the whole problem in traumatology—it's surgical indecision. Pity the poor patient. The change has got to come. But I suppose they've been saying that for 25 years."

□

It was 6:25 P.M., the same evening the young man died. Peggy Palmer had run the quarter of a mile to the helicopter pad atop the parking garage. She stood on the eighth-story roof, her arms wrapped around her body for warmth as she scanned the steel gray March sky for a sign of the incoming helicopter. Three minutes passed. Then, first a speck on the southwest horizon, then a whirling roar and a rush of wind, and the Belljet Ranger landed like a hummingbird on a large red cross at center roof. Before 30 seconds passed, or the engine had stopped, members of the admitting team removed the accident victim (this time a young woman) from the helicopter and were giving plasma and administering external cardiac massage. She was as badly injured as the young man. With the woman and trauma team aboard, the waiting Baltimore Fire Department Ambulance screamed down through the garage to the emergency entrance of the hospital, where, once again, the patient was rushed through the corridors, along the painted red line, and into the elevator to the first floor admission area. Seventeen minutes after helicopter touch down, the young woman was on the table and the frantic work was under way. "Are you pumping [on the heart]," a doctor asked Miss Palmer.

"Yes," she replied.

"Well stop for a second," the doctor told her, as he watched the monitor for some sign of activity.

"A second is all you get," Peggy Palmer replied, as she again began pumping. But the pumping, pounding, and haste were all in vain. Again, the race was lost. The woman was dead. She was dead when she was picked up by the helicopter in western Maryland. She was still dead after medical science had offered her its best shot. The work stopped.

It was shortly after 8 P.M. An operating room technician had just finished signing over the bodies of the young woman and the young man to two Baltimore morgue attendants. He walked into the lounge near the operating room, slowly shaking his head. He looked around and said, to no one in particular, "You know it's a bad night when the morgue says 'thank you.'"

5

This Unit Plays God
Every Time It Saves Somebody

"I wrote in my notes that I would look into the feasibility
[of removing Karen Ann Quinlan from the respirator], and if I
had found a case that followed medical tradition that I could
have relied on in this circumstance ... then I would have
honored their request .... Well, I investigated and I had to try to
find out some people who had more experience, and I couldn't
find anyone. I had mentioned to Mr. Quinlan that I was going to
get more opinions, to see if I could get more information, to see
if there weren't any cases that might support the Church's
contention .... I called ... after I spoke with several
neurologists ... and said that I personally empathized with [the
Quinlans] I knew what they were going through. I said, 'I cannot
break medical tradition.' "

> *Dr. Robert Morse, Karen Ann Quinlan's attending
> neurologist, testifying under oath in New Jersey Superior
> Court that he could not find a precedent for allowing her
> death, October 20, 1975.*

On February 19, 1974, the clinical director, associate clinical
director, and psychiatric consultant of the Maryland Institute
of Emergency Medicine—the Shock Trauma Unit—told me
that four times in the preceding year physicians in the unit

had turned off respirators which were sustaining the lives of quadriplegics. These were patients, the physicians said, who were totally paralyzed from the base of the skull down and who had absolutely no control over their bodies. They could not even swallow. But these were patients who could see, hear, think, and, had they not had respirator tubes protruding from their throats, they could have spoken. These were not Karen Quinlans, lost in a sleep from which they would never emerge, yet their life-sustaining respirators were turned off. The three senior physicians did not tell me this in confidence. It was not some dark secret, something of which they were ashamed. It was said "on the record," for public consumption. And news of the way those doctors practice medicine was carried on front pages across the country.

□

"The decisions, we've found, in this unit, are relatively easy to make with mature physicians, with people who have reached a point of seniority in their specialty where they know the limitation to the hope of miracles. And I think once you reach that stage, it becomes fairly easy to make the decisions," Dr. T. Crawford McAslan told me. Dr. McAslan, an anesthesiologist and the unit's associate clinical director, went on to say that "The problem you have is with the younger man who doesn't feel his experience comes up to making such a decision because he just hasn't seen all of life, and division of opinion is the biggest problem. We are perhaps fortunate in this unit in having a group of relatively mature specialists in every area, so I think we largely agree on every decision .... You have to know what it is for a family to be handicapped by some severely handicapped person, either mentally or physically or both. You have to know this can seriously destroy a family, either financially or psychologically, that it can influence the happiness of other, normal, people in the household. Perhaps they can't go to work because they've got to stay home [and care for the patient] and you have to have seen this several times with your own eyes, and be aware of these things which are not taught in medical school."

"The second thing," said Dr. McAslan, "is you've got to have enough experience of medicine to have encountered cases similar to the one you're considering, not once, but on many occasions, and you know what the outcome is going to be. And you know this talk of one in a million [cures] is often not proven by fact but is often just handed down from one physician to another. They've heard of one case where a person made it . . . . But if you're familiar with the literature and clinical practice, you know that in fact this is not true, so you can afford to back up your decisions with social feelings and maturity of judgement. This becomes easy for the mature man but very difficult for the young man."

"This is the point with the young physicians," interjected unit director and founder R. Adams Cowley: "They've heard about [the various procedures], they've read about them, and, therefore, [believe] all efforts should be made."

"The doctor does have some responsibility and has to accept some of the responsibility for the decisions," added Dr. Gill, who was then clinical director of the Shock Trauma Unit. "What so frequently happens is everyone is so terrified of the medical-legal implications and criticism from other colleagues that you tend to get a lot of buck passing, and doctors won't stand up and accept some of responsibility."

"That's the core statement," interrupted psychiatrist Nathan Schnaper. "Other doctors will say that the doctors who assume medical responsibility are playing God, but this unit, in a sense, plays God every time it saves somebody."

"Again, we're at an advantage here," Dr. McAslan told me. "When you deal with a group of specialists, as we do, somebody eventually has to make the decision. There has to be a chief."

A little over a year after this discussion took place Dr.
Gill resigned as clinical director of the Shock Trauma Unit in
a dispute with Dr. Cowley over what Gill terms the practice
of "committee medicine." According to Gill, Dr. Cowley
never commented publicly on the dispute; decision-making in
the unit was to be turned over to a committee. At the time of
this interview, however, Gill was the final arbiter of all
decisions regarding the treatment of patients. It was he who
accepted the ultimate responsibility for any decisions to
terminate care. It is ironic, therefore, to look back now and
remember Dr. McAslan, who is still associate clinical director,
telling me: "You know how difficult it is to get a committee
to agree . . . . We have one man who can ultimately weigh out
the feelings of the other people and make the decision."

"I think the worst thing people do in our profession is
they have a tendency to let the patient, or the patient's
family, make the decision," Dr. Cowley told me. Dr.
Schnaper added that he thought allowing the family to make
the decision is "cruel." "You know a family doesn't have the
ability to really make this decision," Dr. Cowley continued.
"They're not trained in the field, and to simply allow the
family to make the decision whether or not you should
continue the therapy is terrible; and yet some physicians do
this."

"The worst part of asking a family to do this is this
leaves the family with the burden of guilt," Dr. Schnaper
added.

"If you tell the family the truth," Dr. Cowley said,
"and, in your experience you've gone and done everything
you can, and this [ending treatment] is what you
recommend, then the family will usually say, 'then doctor,
that's what I want done,' If they don't, they will tell you that
they don't, and you continue treatment."

"It depends on the doctor's presentation," Dr. Gill said.
"Obviously, you can sway a family any way you want; and

this is where the doctor's responsibility comes in. He still has to be honest with them, but you can be honest and still quite clearly indicate the advice that you're giving them, although of course they still have the ultimate say. You never go against the express wish of the family."

How often, I asked the doctors, are you faced with deciding you should give up on a patient?

"I'd say about two percent," Dr. Gill responded, meaning that at least 25 times a year the physicians in the unit decide there is nothing more they can do for a patient, and they give up trying to ward off death. "You tend to let nature take its course," Dr. Gill explained, who said most such patients eventually die of pneumonia. "Any day of the week we will have two such patients. Any day you will go up and see two patients [who are being allowed to die] .... The majority we are still very cautious with and really wait longer than we should—basically wait until the patient is brain dead. If you wait long enough with a hopeless patient on a respirator most of them will become brain dead, and then you have a definition of death. I don't think we've ever taken anyone off a respirator who could go home .... It's all mixed up with the problem of what would happen to the patient, if you have a vegetable. First of all, you can't get that patient out anywhere, there are very few facilities to look after the patient. Most facilities that would care for the patient have a couple of months' waiting list. Now when you have that type of patient, there's usually a marked neurological deficit in terms of cough reflexes, swallowing. You do tend to let nature take it's course," Dr. Gill said.

"You must not falsely give hope to the family," Dr. McAslan said, "once you yourself are quite satisfied there is no hope. You musn't be tempted to offer false hope. I think you're often bated into this if you're not experienced. They'll say, 'there's not the slightest chance of recovery?' And if you're wise, you'll say, 'not the slightest chance.'

Whereas, if you're a younger man, you may say, 'there's a
one in one million chance,' and they'll grasp at that and say
'take the one in a million.' "

"Each doctor," said William Gill, picking up the
conversation, "has a responsibility to the community, as well
as to the patient."

"What we haven't touched on." Dr. McAslan responded,
"and I know people don't like to talk about this, but we have
to talk about it, is money . . . . You must think in terms of
how much money society should spend on supporting the life
of this type of individual. Whether we like to talk about this
or not [we must consider]: Is there money available or isn't
there money avilable? Are there facilities? Should we spend,
are we morally correct in spending money [on these
patients] when we can take a child from the ghetto with a
[repairable heart defect] and give that same amount of
money and produce a productive, healthy, child with a
future life ahead of him, a normal life? Is it morally right to
expend the money, and the funding available in this country
isn't infinite. We shouldn't kid ourselves that it's infinite. It's
finite. How do we spend this money. I'm not presenting this
as we view it: I'm posing this to society as a problem," Dr.
McAslan said. "We don't view this from a financial angle. We
don't say that because a person can afford to pay for good
care we keep him alive. I'm saying to society that this is a
very real problem. How are we going to spend this nation's
wealth? And I think this should be, has to be, at the back of
one's mind when you consider these questions."

"Does the family ever know what the bill will be
before they get it," I asked.

"Money is never discussed," Dr. Gill responded. "The
state absorbs the cost. All patients get exactly the same
therapy. It's all strictly medical. Later on, if it turns out they
can't pay the bill, then the state absorbs it. . . . The bills
in the unit," he continued, "can reach astronomical

proportions, accumulating, as they do, at the rate of $575 a day—for the bed alone—in the critical care area. There was one woman, Dr. Gill said, who received a bill for $20,000, for just the bed. "But she had every bone, every major bone in the body, broken, plus severe chest injuries, major vessel eruption in the chest and several abdominal injuries, and this woman, the mother of several children, eventually went home. And she's functioning today. The point is, here was a woman who had this money spent on her. When we started on her she was a totally broken body. Now she is a mother taking care of her family . . . . Where are you going to stop, you see?"

"So what you're saying is that society has to decide if there comes a point when you turn off the machines because you can't afford . . ."

Dr. McAslan interrupted me: "Society must take care of this type of problem for people . . . . That's what I'm saying. Society has to accept the fact that we *do* have *fixed* resources. Society has to accept that this type of catastrophic accident victim has to become a charge of the state. And, thirdly, society also has a right to say how much it is willing to expend on hopeless cases." We must, Dr. McAslan was saying, be willing to back up doctors in their decision of when to stop giving such care to the people that are not going to come back into society and contribute.

"Money is involved, for example, if somebody is paralyzed from the chin down and the family then wants to go to a place like Los Alamos where they wire up the patient's eyelids and so on to operate an electrified wheel chair," Dr. Schnaper said. "All that is fantastically expensive, so money plays a part there, too. However, what we're talking about now does not enter into the decisions" relating to care in the unit on a day to day basis.

I turned our conversation, at one point, back to a discussion of the withdrawal of care from quadriplegics. "Let me make sure I understand this clearly," I said. "When you have a quadriplegic, and you've come to the conclusion that you can't do anything more for them, that their condition isn't going to improve, you make the decision to turn off the respirator?"

Before responding directly to my question, the doctors were quick to point out the kind of patient they were referring to when they spoke of quadriplegics. These were not, they stressed, persons whose arms and legs were paralyzed, but who could breathe on their own and had control of some shoulder and chest muscles. These were not the type of patients who could eventually make use of portable respirators and wheel chairs. These patients, whose spinal cords were severed, or damaged beyond repair, just below the base of the skull, were nothing more than brains imprisoned in bodies—not unlike the living brain in the jar in the standard B horror movie. The physicians said that these patients are first given "aggresive therapy and are carefully followed to see if they are improving or deteriorating. You know the person's in there thinking and perhaps hearing," they said, "but there's just nothing you can do to get him functioning again anyway."

"There's no way a person like this can ever breathe again on his own," Dr. McAslan said. "The lungs will not breathe. And, therefore, he is sentenced to the machine to keep him alive. He's attached to the machine, as long as that machine functions. But he's in trouble because it's subject to all the mechanical failures—if someone trips over the cord, and so forth. So this man is sentenced to the rest of his life to this precarious artificial existence, and he still cannot dress himself, feed himself. He can do nothing except above the neck. And with this type of individual, when we have established all this, and there will be no further improvement, I think it's fair to say that we feel therapy should not be continued."

"It's not quite as clear cut as that," Dr. Gill replied. "If you have a patient who is quadriplegic, and he rapidly becomes aware of it and says, 'I want to live' then you're not going to shut off the respirator."

"So we're talking about patients who don't communicate with you?"

"Yes. If the quadriplegic doesn't communicate, and the whole problem has been discussed with the family, and we have waited long enough to be absolutely certain of diagnosis, and the patient cannot live without the respirator, then he's removed from the respirator."

"Have you had quadriplegics who could talk to you, who said 'I don't want to go on this way, take me off the machine?' "

"The majority indicate that," Dr. Gill replied.

"A person who is quadriplegic essentially has sensations reaching his brain cut off," Dr. McAslan said, "and when you remove sensations going into your brain, the incoming messages, you go to sleep. If you make a person free of cold, free of noise, free of sensations, the person is, in effect sedated. In that sense, they are not truly as alert as you would be."

"But aren't there some who have communicated, who have said, 'I know you can keep me going like this, but I don't want to live?'

"I cannot recall a single person in this category who has ever expressed a desire to live," Dr. McAslan said, staring hard at me.

"But how many have expressed a desire to die?"

"I think about two [of the four]," William Gill said. "Two became very introverted, I think really, and they didn't want ... "

"They didn't necessarily have to communicate it verbally," said psychiatrist Nathan Schnaper, "but it's obvious. They withdraw into themselves." '

"Yes, but you're talking about patients who have no communication. So you and the family decide it's time to quit."

"You have communication with most of the quadriplegics," Dr. Gill responded.

"But you don't ask them if they want to die," Dr. McAslan said. "What that would really be asking them is if they want you to shoot them. It's like saying to anyone, 'you're not going to get out of this building, do you mind if I put a bullet in your head?' It would be inhumane to force this question. To actually pose this question . . . ." Dr. McAslan paused to collect his thoughts, saying that he wanted to make his response very clear, but was having difficulty phrasing it. "You cannot pose a question, either to the patient or a relative . . . . Everyone dearly loves life; and every relative and brother and sister, if posed with the question, 'do you want us to keep your brother alive,' there are very few who would say, 'no. Kill him.' "

"I personally, as a doctor, would find it almost at odds with my ethics as a doctor, certainly with my Hippocratic oath, to approach a patient and take away all hope of life," Dr. Gill said. "I have never in my life done that, and I doubt that I ever will, because I regard that as inhumane and without compassion, and compassion is one of the fast disappearing elements that a physician should have."

"But isn't turning off a respirator, which is maintaining the life of a thinking, alert, human being, killing them? Aren't you doing something active to them rather than just stopping a course of treatment?"

"It's not active, really," Dr. Gill responded. "It was active to start the treatment, you see? You initiated the artificial treatment, and this is done every day" in open heart operations.

"This therapy, this unusual therapy, was initiated, or they would have died," Dr. McAslan explained. "We said, we'll use this tool [the respirator] until we evaluate them fully, to give us time to make up our minds about this patient. So you could argue we should never have put them on it in the first place. All we're doing is deciding to take away the artificial support."

"It's illegal, I suppose some people argue that," Dr. Gill said during a conversation I had with him about a week later, "but it can best be compared to our resuscitating a patient near death, opening them up, and then finding there's nothing we can do. You have a situation where the patient cannot live without the respirator—a large number would actually die even if they were left on the respirator. Now I know of no organization that can provide unlimited respirators to keep patients alive. We have emergencies coming in here all the time. But that isn't why the decision is made .... But you're not actively doing anything to worsen the patient's state according to what that state was when the patient comes in here. All you are doing is using artificial support to see if you can do something and then you withdraw that support when you find there is nothing you can do. We use that rationalization in our own minds."

I told the doctors that I had heard a story about a quadriplegic patient in the unit who didn't seem to be reacting to any stimuli and was taken off the machine. Then, a source had told me, the patient moved a finger.

"There have been instances when we have reversed on a decision," Dr. Gill responded, "wrongly in almost every case. And we've had to go back to the original decision. But the [first reversal of the decision to withdraw treatment] has been based on a very emotional response, usually from a nurse, who insists that she has elicited certain responses. And, of course, once that happens, you have no choice but to go back and aggressively treat the patient until the accurate determination becomes obvious."

"But I've been told there are some staff members who feel you're too quick to make these determinations, that the decisions have become too easy for you," I told the doctors.

"No, they haven't," Dr. McAslan responded for the group. "But your observation may be true that there are all grades of people here from the rather extensive senior staff right down to all grades of medical students to lay observers occasionally, different grades of people, many of whom are not prepared for an area like this. They may be having a preliminary exposure, maybe as young medical students. Now obviously many of these people, including many of the nurses, who rotate through here as their first experience right out of nursing school, are just not up to this. And this is a democracy. They are entitled to express their opinions, but that doesn't make them right. You know, in an area like ours, you do have a certain psychological stress on the nurses and..."

"We talked about parents having guilt," Dr. Schnaper said, "if they were given the responsibility of deciding. I've heard, here and there, a nurse—and of course, the nurses have to keep checking the patients—a nurse bitch about the fact that the doctors aren't using aggressive therapy. 'Why don't they check every ten minutes,' that sort of thing. So it's the nurses' feelings of guilt and responsibility. On the other hand, I've also overheard a nurse say, 'why don't they take Mr. Johnson out of bed four? Why don't they pull the plug on him?' It could be the same nurse making both types of comment .... It's not easy to work in a unit like this. It's physically demanding and psychologically and emotionally very demanding work. For somebody to be here for any length of time, and I'm not a physician, all I do is observe what goes on here, you have to really come with a very deep reverence for life to begin with, or you won't survive. You really have to have a reverence for everybody's life."

"Granted that you consult with various specialists before you decide to turn off a respirator, or stop feeding, or stop administering antibiotics, so some of the responsibility is shared. But what," I asked, "do you think about afterwards?"

"It doesn't weigh on my mind," Dr. McAslan responded.

"Does it weigh on your mind before hand?"

"Oh, yes," replied all the doctors, virtually in unison.

"It's a very, very difficult decision that is made slowly," Dr. McAslan said.

"But can't you make a wrong decision?"

"I'm sure we can," he replied.

"Does that wear on your mind, that you might have made the wrong decision?"

"I don't know when any decision has not been unanimous," Dr. Schnaper said, not quite answering the question.

"Medicine is never 100 percent sure on any decision," Dr. McAslan said.... "What I'm talking about is that a doctor has to accept this in his own soul. And his decision as to diagnosis, his decisions as to treatment, are always made with the best information that he can have both from observing a patient, from examining a patient, from testing a patient, and from all the knowledge he can glean from his experiences, and from the knowledge he can glean from his colleagues, if it's an area he's not very sure about. And only once you have explored every avenue of expertise, do you make a decision. You have to learn, in medicine, to make decisions. You have to learn to make a decision right, or wrong, after weighing out all the facts.... And then you stick to that decision unless there's some ... '

Nathan Schnaper cut in: "It's like a lawyer working out a case. Once the case is done, it's on to the next case."

"But this involves life and death."

"So does a soldier leading someone into battle," Dr. Gill responded. "The planning of a battle, the planning of any of these things. The airline pilot used to make these decisions when he'd land. If you're in a responsible position in life ... you cannot occupy such a position unless you're capable, hopefully capable, of making alot more correct decisions than wrong decisions. And the longer you go on in life you would hope that the more right decisions you'd make. Certainly, this is a job with responsibilities. The patient's life is in your hands. You're given the degree and you're given the legal right to take patients' lives into your hands. And you've certainly got to feel you've got this responsibility and then you've got to prove your ability to use the knowledge that you have earned and gotten that legal right to practice. I think your teachers have a big say in your learning humility. Your family has a big say in this. If your teachers are willing to accept defeat openly, and say, 'I can't do any more for this patient,' and you hear this, and the teacher doesn't present himself as omnipotent. And I think the young man today probably has bigger problems because he lives in a world where everything appears to be finite. You can put a man on the moon. It appears you can almost solve every problem. And it's difficult not to apply this to the maximum and think that every problem *is* solvable. And it's only after you really look around in medicine and see in truth how little we can sometimes offer people for the major killers today: trauma, heart disease, cancer, and stroke. And you realize that the most we can offer to many of these people is comfort and support rather than cure."

Throughout our discussion I had gotten the impression that the patient's relatives really played very little part in the decision to withhold treatment. Wasn't this, I asked, an example of the sort of omnipotence which the physicians said they had to strive to avoid?

"No," Dr. McAslan replied. "Every death, whether it

happens at two months of age or happens at 100 years of age, whether it happens with prior warning, or happens unexpectedly, is always faced with remorse, unhappiness, and guilt. You ruminate over things you might have done when the person was alive. You're going to have this with any death, because you never live life the way it should be lived. So it's foolish to me to drag people through the inquisition of whether they should let someone die. *I think it's just as great a punishment to be left looking at a reminder of your errors in the form of a living hell, as it is to look at a tombstone, or a memory you had, and it's a case of how you look at your reminders of mistakes in your past life.*

□

The week after the New Jersey Supreme Court handed down its decision in the Quinlan case, I went back to Baltimore to speak with Dr. Gill, who is now in private practice there. I wondered how he felt about the Quinlan decision, and what, if any, repercussions he had suffered as a result of the publication two years earlier of some of the things he and his colleagues had told me about withdrawing life support.

"I think that the opinion that alot of people are giving now—that this should remain a medical decision—is the one that I would adhere to," he told me. "I have also reflected upon the repercussions of my comments the last time around . . . . I would be very much more guarded in everything I said and how I said it, as a result of some of the sequela to some very frank comments. What is clear is that if a doctor, who obviously has certain professional and ethical obligations to his medical society, and community, etc., if he speaks too frankly a reflection of his own personal opinion, there is little doubt he can be called to task for it. And, I suppose, in a way, that might be justified."

"What are you referring to? How were you called to task?"

"After your articles appeared, first of all there was a mass of mail. I would think it was probably divided 80 or 90 percent in favor, the rest, 10 percent or so, was against us. Some of the letters that were critical were constructive. I had letters from quadriplegics and paraplegics who said some of the things I said were inaccurate, based on their own experience, and I can't argue with that . . . . The most critical letters were from societies like the Right to Life society. Many of those that were in favor were from the relatives of quadriplegics and paraplegics, and many were from nurses. One that particularly sticks in my mind from a nurse stated something about passing the buck. She had quite a horror story to tell, and said 'thank goodness somebody doesn't pass the buck,' in terms of not making a decision for months and months.

"I was asked to appear before the local medical society, as a result of a letter they'd received from the Right to Life society. I was, very pleasantly, asked to explain what my position was and what my ethics were, how I dealt with such problems. There seemed to be special emphasis placed on whether the problem was discussed with the patient and with the relatives. They simply wanted me to establish that in cases I'd been personally involved in, I'd discussed the problem and hadn't gone off on a tangent. They accepted my comments, and they appeared satisfied.

"What I regard as my duty as a doctor," Gill told me, "if I'm managing a patient that I think has no hope of surviving—and other people agree with me—then I would regard it as my duty to try to insure that that patient's demise was without any suffering . . . . I've always spoken frankly with the family. I would advise them what I would recommend for my own relatives, and that's what I've always done . . . . The only people qualified to know with certainty that there is no hope for future life are the medical people. And, therefore, it's the medical people who should at least give a very strong opinion."

Knowing of Dr. Gill's abhorrence of what he terms "committee medicine," I asked what he thought of the Supreme Court's ruling that decisions that a case is hopeless must be concurred in by a hospital's ethics committee before care can be withdrawn.

"If I, as a doctor, was a quadriplegic, if I was lying there, and had adequate cerebral function and wanted to know what was going to happen, I would want to speak with three or four physicians who I knew were experienced in this type of management, and I respected, to help me make my decision, if the decision was mine. I would not want, at that particular point for that particular decision, to speak to a priest. I would not want to speak to a psychiatrist. I would not want to speak to a lawyer. I would not want to speak to any layman. I might want to speak to those very valuable people afterwards, for other reasons," he said with a laugh, "but not to decide whether I should tell my medical team 'please go ahead and withdraw.'

But legally clearing the way to withdraw artificial life supports in cases like Karen Ann Quinlan's does not solve all the problems, or comparable problems, Dr. Gill told me. "What do you do for the patient who is literally dying from cancer, or a malignancy, with no cure in sight, and experience tells you that patient may be around for a few weeks in a distressing state? In fact, I had a very personal experience with my mother, who was dying of advanced breast cancer. I was consulted over the phone by several surgeons in charge of her who had her under heavy sedation. They wanted to know if I wanted the sedation lightened, because if that degree of sedation was kept up, then the end was not very far away. If they lightened the sedation, she might live a few weeks longer. I told them to keep up the sedation . . . . "

Part Four

THE INFANTS

6

There Is No Wrong Decision

Mr. Coburn: Is it possible for you to give a mental age—when I talk about "mental age," I'm talking of the cognitive age of Karen's condition. Can you characterize her reflex, everything you've seen as far as Karen's cognitive function in a stage such as a two-week-old infant, five-week-old infant, seven-year-old child, or something like that?

Dr. Korein: It would be inaccurate, but I would make an attempt. Do you wish me to make an attempt?

Mr. Coburn: Yes.

Dr. Korein: The best way I can describe this would be to take the situation of an anencephalic monster. An anencephalic monster is an infant that's born with no cerebral hemisphere . . . . If you take a child like this, in the dark, and you put a flashlight in the back of the head, the light comes out the pupils. They have no brain. Okay?

The only sound in the courtroom was that made by the pens and pencils of more than 100 reporters as they furiously scribbled the exchange in their notebooks. The usually

unflappable, pugnacious, Daniel Coburn was visibly shocked
by Dr. Julius Korein's answer to his question. There was
Coburn who was clearly trying to elicit a reply which would
allow him to compare Karen Ann Quinlan to a cute, cuddly,
newborn baby but instead heard a graphic description of a
human jack-o'-lantern. Much to Coburn's credit, since he was
trying to "save" Karen's life, he did not ask Dr. Korein how
the medical profession generally responds to the birth of an
"anencephalic monster." And regrettably, neither did Paul
Armstrong, who was attempting to convince Judge Muir that
there was no moral or medical obligation to preserve Karen
Ann Quinlan's remaining life. For the remainder of the trial I
kept thinking of that unasked, unanswered question: "Dr.
Korein, you just testified that, if you had to make a
comparison, you would compare Karen's cognitive function
to that of an anencephalic monster. Doctor, how are such
infants treated? Are they kept alive? Are they fed? Do their
parents ever take them home from the hospital?"

Had Paul Armstrong asked that question, the absurdity
of maintaining Karen Ann Quinlan's life would have quickly
become as apparent as the absurdity of claiming no precedent
could be found for allowing her death. For all over America,
every day, physicians in delivery suites and intensive care
nurseries stand by and intentionally allow the deaths of
infants who are physically and mentally horribly deformed
but are, in most cases, better off than Karen Quinlan was. In
some cases they advise parents against authorizing potentially
life-saving surgical intervention. At other times they may
simply tell a couple that their child died at birth and
withhold food from the infant. In some cases these infants
are so grossly deformed that their image remains sharply
engraved in the minds of the physicians and hospital
personnel who helped deliver them. Dr. Korein, for instance,
told me of a situation in which he was personally involved as
a young doctor. "Early in my career," he said, "I delivered

about 40 to 70 children, babies, in my medical student and internship and so on . . . . and there was one situation where the woman gave birth to twins. One child was normal and one child was a monstrosity. When I say monstrosity," he paused for an instant, "the best way I can describe this child, it was like a bird—birdlike claws, feet, and a beak, with eyes almost run together and the head horribly misshapen. This was a monstrosity in the ultimate sense. That monstrosity was breathing. Now at that point—talk about value judgments—I took the monstrosity and put in a bassinet, put it in the corner, and put a sheet over it. The nurse went over to touch it and I said, 'don't touch it! Just don't touch it!' That's all. Now that was judicious neglect. That's an example of it."

"How long did it take it to die?"

"By the time we looked the next time it was no longer breathing. There was no attempt to make it breathe, no attempt to help it breathe or anything. I think that would have been criminal. Now, I wasn't about to say that in court (during the Quinlan trial). But I never told the mother of the monster," Dr. Korein continued. "I got hold of the father and said, 'they were twins. One child is perfectly normal, healthy. The other was somewhat malformed and expired.' Now, did I commit a criminal act? I'm not going to say," he responded to his own question. "By the way, there was another time when I delivered a baby with meningomyelocele," an opening in the spinal column and protrusion of part of the spine, often accompanied by hydrocephalus, or 'water on the brain,' . . . . "But that kid was breathing," Dr. Korein continued, "and there was no way [to withhold care] unless you were going to actively do something to kill that child. I do not believe in killing. I don't want to get into the business of euthanasia, where you say 'O.K., this person is in this kind of state so we're going to kill him.' But they didn't want to get into that at the trial; they said active and passive [response to a life threatening situation] are not different. Well, they are different: It's easy to say don't resuscitate. Once you resuscitate, it's very difficult to stop resuscitation."

Every so often we read newspaper accounts about court cases involving parents, usually Jehovah's Witnesses, who have refused, on religious grounds, to allow blood transfusions or similar treatments for their ailing children. And in those cases, courts have generally held that doctors may proceed with the treatment because the state has an interest in, and duty to, protect life; an interest and duty which overrides the parents' right to practice their religion. Those cases are generally very straight forward—the child involved is usually suffering from some easily correctable problem and can be expected to recover fully if the disputed treatment is administered.

Problems involving severely defective infants, however, rarely get to court, for parents and doctors are generally in accord on the treatment of such cases. These are not, it must be stressed, infants who are what the average person would think of as mentally retarded. Nor are they physically deformed in such a way that they will grow up to be some year's brightly smiling March of Dimes poster child. One in every thirteen babies born in the United States suffers from some form of birth defect—from something as simple as a harelip to as devastating a condition as anencephaly. And the vast majority of these children, with or without corrective surgery (if such treatment is possible), will go on to live meaningful lives, lives at the least filled with self-awareness and awareness of their surroundings, no matter how basic and simple that awareness may be. But there are other infants who, if they are saved, are little more than human plants. There are no national statistics on the subject, but I learned that, in the Washington, D.C., area alone, at least once a week the decision is made to allow the death of such an infant.

These are infants who are so severely retarded they will never be able to function for themselves on even the most rudimentary level and will never be able to relate to other human beings, even on as simple a level as a pet relates to its owner. They are victims of the ravages of extreme Downs Syndrome, commonly known an Mongolism, and in addition to that suffer from major physical anomalies, such as defective hearts or other problems requiring extensive, expensive, life-saving surgery. They may also be infants who are grossly deformed physically, not unlike the bizarre case described by Dr. Korein that need surgery to survive.

"Our old criteria of death dealt with the heart beat," Dr. Gordon Avery told me. "Whether or not to keep defective babies alive once wasn't such an issue. Now," said Dr. Avery, who is chief of the division of neonatology (infant medicine) at the Childrens' Hospital National Medical Center, in Washington, "we shoot for a meaningful life, rather than how long we can maintain a heart beat. You always have to be helpful, not harmful. And there are times when to do everything you can is to be harmful rather than helpful."

It is difficult to understand how saving a baby might be harmful, unless one is discussing a deformed monster, a truly horrible freak of nature such as the infant delivered by Dr. Korein. But there are times when intervention can be harmful, harmful to the parents as well as to the infant. While cases involving nonintervention in the care of infants rarely end up in court, when they have, they have generally provided excellent examples of why the cases shouldn't have been in court, and why the parents and doctors should have been left alone to make their own decision as best they could. The ordeal of Kay and Michael Teague provides one of the most recent object lessons along those lines, for in her brief seven weeks of life, Samantha Teague became caught up in a tug of war between her parents and the state of Maryland.

The moment of Samantha Teague's birth should have been one of particular joy; two parents, in a hospital delivery room, together witnessing the entrance into the world of their second, planned child. But as the doctor guided Samantha Lara Jean Teague from her mother, it was immediately clear that something was wrong. "I know exactly what you said," Kay Teague said to her husband as the three of us later discussed that moment: it was, " 'Oh, my God! What's the matter with her feet?' " Samantha's club feet and deformed legs were the least of her problems. She was also suffering from spinabifida (an opening in the base of the spine), hydrocephalus, and a nonfunctioning bladder. An estimated .002 percent of the babies born each year in the United States suffer from spinabifida, and in the majority of cases the condition is operable and the babies grow up into relatively normal children, although they are often permanently crippled. But in some cases, such as Samantha's fluid has built up on the brain so rapidly that it has caused massive, irreparable brain damage before surgery can be performed to relieve the pressure.

In an effort to find help for Samantha, Kay and Michael Teague took their newborn infant to the Children's Hospital National Medical Center where they consulted with Dr. Thomas Herrick Milhorat, chief of neurosurgery. In a deposition prepared for, but never used, in Baltimore (Md.) Circuit Court, Dr. Milhorat said he had operated on, and cared for, more than 250 children suffering from spinabifida. Referring to patients as severely afflicted as Samantha, he wrote: "personal experience, as well as that documented in medical literature, indicate that such patients never become normally functioning individuals . . . . In our own clinic it is felt that operative procedures on [such seriously afflicted] patients . . . are unjustified. In such cases . . . treatment other than that to assure the comfort of the infant is avoided," wrote Dr. Milhorat. Faced with physicians' opinions that

Samantha's chances of surviving would be very poor even with surgery, faced with the fact that her head had already swollen seven eighths of an inch in her first 24 hours of life and she would be severely retarded even if she survived, the Teagues decided against authorizing surgery for their daughter.

"We didn't accept the options immediately," said Michael Teague.

"You can't agree with somebody's opinion like that!" said Kay Teague, snapping her fingers for emphasis. As she and Michael spoke to me in the comfortable living room of their suburban townhouse, their first child, Sean, then three, played noisily in the next room.

"It seemed to us the physical handicap would be much easier to cope with, both for the parents and the child," Michael Teague said. "It's the mental . . . " His voice trailed off and he didn't finish the sentence.

Told that Samantha would live anywhere from a few days to a few months, the Teagues began looking for an institution where their daughter could be cared for during her remaining days. After being turned down at one Maryland state facility, which has an excellent reputation, "because we lived in the wrong county," as Kay said, the couple succeeded in having Samantha placed in Rosewood, a state institution for the mentally retarded. Even then, "we had to argue to get her in," said Michael, "they said they'd never had a child that young."

Shortly after placing Samantha in Rosewood, the Teagues discovered, as have many similarly situated parents, that institutionalizing such a child in a state facility can be the beginning, rather than the ending, of their problems. Only three days after leaving Samantha at Rosewood, Kay Teague received a call from the chief of pediatrics there, who "said the child would be admitted to University Hospital [in Baltimore] and she indicated at that point that she felt

surgery would be worthwhile." Kay and Michael took
Samantha to the hospital themselves, where she was
examined by a surgeon "who said there was a reasonable
chance that with surgery she would have a normal
intelligence level at age two to four," Michael said. "We took
those figures back to the other doctors and they did not
agree with the prognosis." Again, the couple refused to
authorize surgery for Samantha.

The next thing the Teagues heard from the state was
that the attorney general's office was going into court to have
Samantha made a temporary ward of the state in order that
surgery be authorized. Because Kay and Mike were given only
two hours' notice prior to the hearing, their attorney
managed to obtain a delay of two days. As the hearing was
about to begin on a Friday morning, the judge received word
that Samantha was too weak to undergo surgery, and the
court test was postponed again. The following Sunday
morning, Samantha Lara Jean Teague died, and the case was
never settled.

I asked Ted Lucas, chief of Maryland's Mental
Retardation Administration and the man who initiated the
court case, why he felt it necessary to subject the Teagues,
and for that matter, Samantha, to such an ordeal. "It is my
philosophy that every child has a potential, regardless of the
degree of mental retardation. If the child is placed in the
custody of the state to render a service, the state will do
everything to render [that service]," said Mr. Lucas, who is
an administrator, not a physician. "We went to court in order
to get the authority to do what needed to be done in order
for the potential of this child to be realized." I asked him
what Samantha's potential was, what chance such a grossly
retarded child would have of ever leaving the institution, or
leading anything remotely resembling a meaningful life,
meaningful even to her. The administrator said that that was
an "undetermined factor . . . . As long as the child is given
over to the state to assist him, we must give the child as much

humane assistance as possible." This, it seemed to me, was clearly a case where, to use Dr. Avery's words, "to do everything you can is to be harmful, rather than helpful."

Despite the fact that they expected Samantha's death, Kay and Michael Teague did not find it easy to take. For she was, despite her deformities, their child. "I didn't know what to say," Kay told me. "The fact that we knew she'd die didn't make it any easier. I felt incredibly sad."

"It's like somebody hit you with a brick wall," Michael said of receiving the news. "The fact that one does what one believes is in her best interest does not make it any easier," he said, speaking very softly. "When you have a medical problem of this kind, I think the state has a right to get involved, but it doesn't gain anything" by doing so, even if it wins a court case.

□

Although the state occasionally intervenes in such cases, it is much more frequent that they go humanely unnoticed. In an article entitled "Moral and Ethical Dilemmas in The Special-Care Nursery" in the *New England Journal of Medicine,* October 25, 1973, doctors Raymond S. Duff and A.G.M. Campbell said that "of 299 consecutive deaths occurring in a special-care nursery, 43 [14 percent] were related to withholding treatment. These infants, cared for in the special-care nursery of the Yale-New Haven [Connecticut] Hospital, were so severely retarded or deformed those caring for them felt there was 'little or no hope' [for them to] achieve meaningful 'human-hood,' . . . For example, they have little capacity to love or be loved. They are often cared for in facilities that have been characterized as 'hardly more than dying bins,' an assessment with which, in our experience, knowledgeable parents [those who visited chronic-care facilities for the placement of their children] agreed."

Dr. David Abramson, chief of neonatology and the intensive care nursery at the Georgetown University Medical Center in Washington told me that "in 99 percent of our cases we have to make a conscious decision to let the baby go." It should be noted that Dr. Abramson's unit is a referral center for the Metropolitan Washington area, and, therefore, he sees only the sickest babies. And of those infants, in about two thirds of the cases, there is no chance of saving the baby, and the decision is simply one of when to turn off the electronic equipment that is sustaining the infant's pitiful semblance of life. But about 20 times a year, Dr. Abramson must tell a pair of distraught parents that he feels it would be pointless, indeed, wrong, to operate or continue treatment that might save their infant perhaps for weeks, perhaps months, or even years. I asked David Abramson, himself the father of three children, when did he tell fellow parents that he believes it best that he cease attempting to save their child, and he said very matter-of-factly, "When you want the patient to die, and not live." He continued, "Every time a doctor sees a patient he has to think, 'What do I want for this patient?' Most of the time we just assume that the patient should be kept alive. But it's the first question [I ask myself] when a person is seriously ill. All infants deserve the best medical care until they convince us that their potential for a meaningful life is negligible, and I'm pretty hard to convince." Dr. Abramson said that before he considers withdrawing treatment from an infant he has to consider what sort of life that infant will live if he saves it. "My basic value is, if I believe that infant is going to be able to give and receive love, we ought to make every attempt to save the baby's life. Mongoloids," he said, "would fall within those bounds. Mongoloid children can certainly give and receive love and should not be allowed to die simply because they're Mongoloids."

As is the case with severely ill and dying adults, the debate over whether to save defective infants often comes down to the semantic argument over the meaning of the words "ordinary" and "extraordinary" means of preserving life. "We have to draw a distinction between ordinary and extraordinary means," said Dr. Avery of Children's Hospital. "We never withdraw what's needed to make a baby comfortable, we would never withdraw the care a parent would provide. We never kill a baby . . . . But we may decide certain heroic intervention is not worthwhile."

"Heroic" intervention, said Dr. Abramson, might be something which, under normal circumstances, would be considered mundane, such as the administration of as basic an antibiotic like penicillin. "If you have a baby who is severely retarded, who is born with various other problems (like an open spinal column), and that baby gets meningitis, it might be extraordinary, heroic, to give that baby penicillin for the meningitis."

The doctors to whom I have spoken over the past several years about the problems of withdrawing care from infants have all told me that often their most difficult problem is assessing an infant's chances of future development. Dr. Phillip Calcagno, director of pediatrics at Georgetown, can still remember the time more than 20 years ago when, while working in a hospital in upstate New York, he "went and saw a baby and called it a mongoloid baby" on the basis of its appearance and behavior. "It was sent to a state home. About a year later, the parents came to see me and said, 'Do you know who we are? You told us our baby was mongoloid.' Well, the baby was completely normal. I don't think you can play God in those situations. You have to take your time."

For Dr. Abramson, the decision to give up on an infant takes "somewhere between 30 seconds and a month. For instance, if the baby is anencephalic, it if gets pneumonia, you know right away" that you don't save it. But while most doctors say the question of whether to save a baby, or for that matter, any patient, is almost always gray, rather than black and white, Dr. Abramson said he believes that "as long as it's gray, your obligation is to save that baby."

"What happens if you make a wrong decision," I asked.

"There can't be a wrong decision," he replied. "It's the best decision you can make. There is no wrong decision. All I am required to do, all I can do, is make the best decision I can, given the information. Can we be wrong about the condition of a baby? Absolutely. But you're not God. You can't play God. You're a human being with human frailties; you just have to make the best decision you can. I don't have an obligation to be right all the time, but I have an obligation to make the best decision. Some of the assumptions may be wrong, and I always present that possibility to the parents . . . . But one alternative isn't right and one isn't wrong. They are both alternatives," David Abramson said.

How, I asked Gordon Avery, does he present the problem to the infant's parents?

"You can't just present yourself as a technician to the family," he told me. "Every single person with a malformed child feels guilty, even though there is not guilt. They shouldn't be [just] confronted with the situation. But by the same token, their feelings have to be taken into consideration. We talk to them, listen to them to get their vibrations, without actually asking them what they want. Some keep pleading with you, 'Isn't there anything you can do? Can't you do more?' And you know where they stand. Another family may say, 'Maybe he'd be better off dead,' or they talk about the stress on the other children, and you know where they stand, too," Dr. Avery continued. "They don't feel it's all their decision; concurring in the recommendation of an expert is much simpler than making a stark, cold, decision themselves."

David Abramson takes a much more direct approach
with parents, an approach which some might consider brutal,
but one which be believes is necessary. While he spends as
much time as possible with the parents, to be as much of a
comfort to them as he can be, at the same time, he believes in
being completely frank and direct with them, and believes
that the final decision to end or withhold treatment is theirs,
and theirs alone. "I don't ask them [if treatment should be
stopped], I tell them," Dr. Abramson explained to me.
"They have known all along where I was. I tell them my
feelings have changed and it's time to stop treatment.
Ninety-nine percent of the time I know what their reaction
will be. But my decision is what *I* want to do. What I *do* is
what the family tells me. But I've never had a family
disagree," he added, in more than 100 cases. And once the
family agrees with Dr. Abramson, he plays devil's advocate.
"I turn around and attack them for letting their baby die.
'You told me you want your baby to die. How does that
make you feel?' Until they're completely ready and able to
handle that, and give me the reasons for the decision, I won't
act.

"I've never made a professional decision I wouldn't
make with my own children," the doctor continued. "The
final question I ask myself is, 'what would I do if this was my
own kid?' It takes a great toll to be with the parents in their
pain. It's very sad when a baby dies. But in the past few years
I've grown comfortable [making such decisions] . . . . I'm
frequently with the baby when he dies, and I haven't gotten
to the point where every one doesn't make me cry. When I
reach that point, I figure I should get out."

Many of the doctors to whom I have spoken have said
that one of the reasons such decisions become necessary at
all, aside from the obvious fact that infants can be kept
technically alive today for whom nothing could have been
done 10 years ago, is the fact that if a couple decides they do

want their severely retarded, crippled infant saved, there are very few places where such a child can be placed. Many couples with other children fear bringing the defective infant home, knowing the disastrous effects such a course of action can have on a marriage and on the development of their normal children. But there are few choices in a society such as ours, which, on the whole, warehouses its old and retarded in institutions which are not much better than those of Charles Dickens' day.

One couple I spoke to told me a tale of bureaucratic horror which provides a perfect example of why decisions to withhold care should not be interfered with. When their infant was born, in a small hospital in suburban Westchester County, New York, it was suffering from spinabifida and hydrocephalus and was already severely retarded. The doctors at the community hospital did not feel qualified to assess the infant's condition, so they sent the parents and their newborn child to a nearby state hospital. Neurosurgeons at the state institution advised operating on the child to relieve the pressure on its brain and save it, but the parents were skeptical. So after the infant had only been in that hospital two days, they checked it out and took it into New York City where it was examined by a group of outstanding neurologists and neurosurgeons, every one of whom advised against operating and said the infant would never be anything more than a vegetable. But the couple told me that when they returned to the state hospital, where they wanted to place their child for his few remaining days, they were told by the director of the institution, "either you sign an authorization for surgery before you leave here today, or you will leave here with your baby and a bill for $20,000" for the days he was there.

"We didn't have any choice," the mother told me, "we had to let them operate." In 1975, as the child approached his fifth birthday, he was, as the couple had been warned, a vegetable, unable to sit up, unable to communicate, unable to respond in any way to human contact and love. The mother has not seen her son since shortly after his birth. Once a year the father went to visit the child in a Catholic home for the retarded in upstate New York, where the state paid for the child's care. But the institution only cares for children under five years of age, and when I spoke to the parents, they (not the state) were frantically trying to find a new home for him. The state, the mother said, told them that placing the child was their responsibility, not New York's. In addition, the couple had moved from New York to Connecticut and were informed they would no longer be eligible for assistance in paying the child's bills. Connecticut told the couple that, as the child was born in New York and originally supported by New York, they were not eligible for aid in their new home. And New York continued to insist that, when the couple moved, their problem moved with them. New York State, which insisted that the child's life be "saved," insisted that it was no longer responsible for the maintenance of that life. So the parents, who had opposed the operation to save their infant, were saddled not only with the responsibility of finding a new home for the child, but of paying his bills as well.

□

Helene Sugarman told me she knew long before her son David was born that there was something very wrong with him. "I had pains so severe I couldn't stand. I told the doctors something was wrong, but they didn't believe me." Helene was right. David was a hydrocephalic. The couple was told "it doesn't look good, but surgery could help," Joel Sugarman told me.

"We weren't even told that, Joel," his wife interjected forcefully. "We were told surgery *would* help." And surgery often does help in such cases. Surgeons were able to insert a tube, called a shunt, which drains the fluid that is building up in the child's skull thereby relieving the pressure on the brain and preventing, or at least minimizing, brain damage. So David Sugarman went home with his parents after the first shunt was inserted and was at home about three weeks when the swelling began again. On July 20, 1971, when he was four days short of being two months old, David was taken back to the hospital. "I took him in," Helene told me, "and the surgeon sat us down and told us the extent of the damage. He said there was so much brain damage the baby would never feel or interpret pain. It would see, but it would never interpret what its eyes saw. It would hear sounds, but it wouldn't be able to interpret the sounds. He would never be more than an infant. The doctor said, 'it's hopeless, but it's your decision.' I said, 'don't operate.' "

"I was optimistic," said her husband. "I pushed for the surgery. I felt that however it came out, we would have a child. It was a difficult thing to go through emotionally . . . "

His wife interrupted, "It was the worst hell anyone can go through. It's something you need to discuss with someone. But in our society, you can't discuss it with anyone because you're damned if you make this decision."

"It was a sword of Damocles hanging over your head that can tear a family apart," said Joel. Both parents told me that had they been given an accurate picture of the situation in the beginning, they would never have authorized the initial, life-saving surgery, and the ordeal would have ended much sooner. As it was, it was to drag on for 10 months. "It was one big nightmare," Helene recalled.

"The hospital would say, 'there's no reason why he can't go home,'" said Joel, "and Helene would panic and say, 'don't send him home!' "

"After David was in the hospital for a while I just stopped going," Helene admitted. "I couldn't go. Yes, he was our son, but there is just so much of yourself you can give in this situation."

Informed by their insurance company that it would no longer pay for David's hospitalization, the Sugarmans had to find an institution in which to place him until his death. After weeks of phone calls, letter writing, and knocking on doors, Helene Sugarman, with the help of Rep. Gilbert Gude (R-Md.), managed to get David placed at Great Oaks, a Maryland state institution for the retarded which is often regarded as a model institution. "I couldn't eat for two days after going out there," Helene told me. "It was very neat, very clean. It's just the tremendous number of damaged youths: four and five years old, diapered, four to a playpen . . . . There was a three-year-old hydrocephalic girl, she was the size of a three-year-old with a head larger than an adult's."

David Sugarman died at Great Oaks, stricken with pneumonia ten months and one week after his birth. "I felt terrible," recalled Helene Sugarman. "My baby was dead. I remember he was little, and had a very large head. But a mother doesn't see that. He was really the most gorgeous hydrocephalic born in a century . . . . He didn't stop being our son . . . . It's something very sad. It's something we've had to deal with. It's something we've had to live through."

"You learn from it," her husband said.

"I wouldn't say that," Helene told me. "You survive it."

7

Diagnostically, She's a Freak of Nature

They all remember it differently. And years afterwards, some choose not to remember it at all. But the agony of deciding to allow the death of a deformed child remains with the child's parents forever. They speak of the inevitability of it all, and say that they did the right thing, took the only rational option. Or they say they simply followed the doctor's lead, that there was no decision to make. But in talking with them for any length of time I quickly come to believe they are tortured by their decision, and their only peace comes in forgetting it. For to remember is to question, and questions are something which their psyches cannot afford. And what is most painful to observe is that they, like Joe and Julie Quinlan, are intellectually very sure of themselves and know they did the right thing, indeed, the *only* thing rationally possible. But being sure in one's mind, and sure in one's heart are two completely different things.

Not having ever had to have made such a choice, it was easy for me to see that the choice they made was the correct one. What made it particularly easy was spending an afternoon talking to a mother who would not even consider making a life and death decision, who said instead that she would do all in her power and in the power of medical science to preserve the life of her horribly deformed daughter. Listening to that mother and seeing her daughter, I could not help but be reminded of Dr. Crawford McAslan's statement that "... it is just as great a punishment to be left looking at a reminder of your errors [in judgment] in the form of a living hell, as to look at a tombstone, or a memory you had."

□

Their memories are in Kodacolor, neatly arranged in rows in a typical family album, pictures of the young husband and wife, their home, their relatives, their friends, and their infant daughter.

A bright-eyed child in a bathinette stares out at a camera as her proud father stands beside her. Written in blue ink in a neat hand is the caption: "The bathing beauty enjoying a first bath." And there they are at the beach—father, daughter, and dog—an instant in time frozen by a loving mother with a camera. The caption: "Kimberly's first trip to the beach house—October 23, 1971." Twenty-two days later, Kimberly was dead.

The odds never really favored Kimberly. She was born with what is known as transposition of the great vessels: the aorta and pulmonary artery were flipflopped, creating two closed circulatory systems within the body, one continuously circulating blood oxygenated between the lungs and the other circulating nonoxygenated blood between the heart and the rest of the body. In addition, Kimberly was also born with a small opening to allow mixture of the oxygenated and nonoxygenated blood. Five years ago, it was necessary to repeat the surgery several times, for the child would be continuously outgrowing the hole, until open heart surgery could be performed about a year after birth. Progress in cardiac surgery has been rapid in this decade, and it is no longer necessary to wait several years before operating in cases like Kimberly's. In fact, corrective surgery can now be performed within weeks, and sometimes even days, of birth.

But such was not the case five years ago, and on November 4, 1971, during that tense year of waiting for the corrective surgery, Kimberly's already fragile system was ravaged by a bacterial infection. "We took her into the hospital on a Monday," Gary, her father, told me, "and her stomach was distended and she looked very sick. They didn't think it was the heart, but she was transfused and everything that night, and by the morning she looked pretty good. But by the time 48 hours had done by . . . . I talked to the doctor and he said, 'there's been massive hemorrhaging, it's destroyed the vital centers of the brain, which control breathing and everything . . . . ' She was already on a hand pump for breathing and he said we could take it away completely, or put her on a respirator. I said, 'No way!' I wouldn't want to live like that."

No matter how long we discussed the events surrounding Kimberly's illness and death, Ginger (Kimberly's mother), and Gary continued to speak of the decision as a nonevent, a simple choice between stopping the use of a hand-operated respirator and placing their daughter on a mechanical device for an uncertain period of time prior to a certain death. But that is not at all the choice the doctor remembered giving the couple. "They had a clear cut choice," he told me. "I told them we could operate on the heart at that point, but she'd be a vegetable, because the control center of the brain was destroyed. Or, we could let her go."

Knowing what the doctor had said, I asked Gary and Ginger if Kimberly could have been kept alive.

"I suppose she could have," replied Gary, "but the doctor said . . . "

"You make it sound like he decided," Ginger quickly interjected. "We decided."

What Kimberly's parents decided was that the hand pump should be taken away and she should be allowed to die. "He said, 'it will take about an hour, so go get a cup of coffee,' " remembered Gary, who, like his wife, discussed the case in a calm, matter of fact manner, like the past history it was. "I said, 'no way,' so he went back and stopped it then. She lived another ten days. But you can't blame the doctor. He said that her heart would go, because that was her problem, right? But that's what kept her alive for ten days, the only thing that functioned. She had a really strong heart.

"The first hour went by, the breathing got very erratic, and then it got less. You could see that the only thing her system was asking was when the heart muscle didn't have enough oxygen it would send a message to the brain to breathe. So breathing became . . . Well, as the days went by the only way you could see she was alive was by the heart monitor."

"Was she being fed," I asked.

"Intravenously for a while, and then, at the end, not at all," replied Ginger. "She held on for 10 days . . . The doctor sait it was very hard for everybody [in the intensive care nursery] and he couldn't let anybody who knew her see her because to feed the baby at that point would kill her, because she had no swallowing reflex. But the doctor said her respiration was so low at that point, that it wasn't really a question of her starving to death because she really didn't need food in that state."

"How did Kimberly's grandparents react to the situation and your handling of it," I asked.

"There were two reactions," said Gary. "One of our sets of parents felt it was best that she died. But the other set said, 'wasn't it nice that she had another 10 days.' It's funny, the different outlook people have. Another 10 days, when at the very end you could only tell she was alive by watching the heart monitor."

"Before Kimberly was born, did you ever think that your baby might have a deformity, or you might have to make the sort of decision you made?"

"I don't think so," Gary said, answering first. "It was our first child and people would ask, 'what do you want, a boy or a girl,' and we'd just say 'a healthy baby,'" he laughed nervously.

"I thought about it, the way any mother does," Ginger said.

I wondered if, three years afterward, there were any lingering doubts or feelings of guilt.

"I never thought of it as a choice," Gary said, "ever. Ever!"

"You ask about guilt," Ginger said. "I sort of wondered if maybe I'd breast fed her, it might have been different; she might have gotten antibodies from me, things like that. You think, maybe if I washed things more carefully. But ... "

Both Ginger and Gary said the hardest thing was being told their daughter would be dead within an hour, and then watching her take 10 days to die. "It was ironic," Ginger said, "because the thing which kept her going was her heart; it was strong, despite all its problems."

One and one-half years after Kimberly died, Ginger gave birth to a second child, a beautiful little girl who suffered from transposition of the great vessels. Researchers do not yet know enough about the formation of the heart to know why some babies, 1 in 6,000, are afflicted with transposition. They do know, however, that the odds against a set of parents having two such babies are about 2,000,000 to 1.

Unlike Kimberly, who was a blue baby, Tracy's color was almost normal when she was born. But she was immediately placed in the intensive care nursery as a precaution. And when the results of her first blood-gas tests came back, the physicians knew they had a problem on their hands—the oxygen content of her blood was much too low. "So the doctor placed her in an isolette with a 100 percent oxygen atmosphere," Gary said. "It should have brought the level in the blood up, but it didn't come up and they said, 'uh, oh,' but they couldn't tell anything for sure until they actually went in and did a catheterization"—a test in which a dye substance is injected into the blood stream and watched as it passes through the heart.

"Can you verbalize what you felt when you heard that?"

"Total anger," Gary said, beginning to show some real emotion for the first time during our discussion. "I was *really* mad. I was mad for about an hour."

"Who, or what, were you mad at?"

"I don't know, I guess God. You know, 'God, why us the second time?' "

"Was there any friction between you," I asked Ginger and Gary, "any exchanging of blame?"

"No," Ginger replied, "we never felt that way. I can remember when the doctors first came in there. Being in the recovery room you're so groggy you don't really know what's going on. But both my births were real easy for me, and so I was lying down there waiting for whatever it was that was going on."

"One of the doctors came down and said Tracy wasn't turning pink right away, that there was something wrong with the lungs. But then they brought me up to my room and said they couldn't find out what was wrong. You were all mad, and everything," Ginger said to her husband, "and then the doctor came down and said, 'we think it's the heart again.' I can remember my reaction being: '*why* us? What have *we* done? Why us?' And then I remember saying I was sorry because I felt bad. Then I looked up at the doctor and she was quiet and she had tears coming down. She didn't know what to do, and that made me feel better, it's the kind of thing where you think somebody cares and you want to comfort them. So then they said I could go up and see the baby. And I saw her, and she looked good, so I had a good feeling about her when I saw her."

Tracy's difficulties were made all the more difficult for Gary, Ginger, their doctors, and the entire staff of the intensive care nursery by memories they still had of Kimberly.

"No one up there could believe it [a second time]," Ginger recalled, explaining that she had become quite close to the nurses in the unit during the days when Kimberly was there. "I stayed there then. They said Kimberly was going to die in an hour and she didn't die. And I came in, we came in together at first for a couple days, and she just kept living and going on, you know, and I came in every morning. It was O.K. at the time, I wanted to be there. I just kind of felt, I don't know how much she knew, I don't think she . . . " Ginger's voice became inaudible, " . . . and I would touch her and stuff. Toward the end it was hard, exhausting. I'd come home and just sleep, completely. It was the type of thing where we knew she was going to die, but it was a matter of not knowing when. And the nurses kind of got used to my being there, being in and out, and they said, 'here, you can clean an isolette or something.' And I got to know the nurses really well."

As Ginger spoke, Tracy, a healthy looking, blond nine-month-old with the saucerlike blue eyes of a Keane painting, sat in her mother's lap quietly playing. Unlike her sister, Tracy didn't have to wait for her open heart surgery, and doctors have told Ginger and Gary that they can expect Tracy to lead a normal, healthy life.

We had almost finished our conversation when, seemingly out of the blue, Gary asked me if I have ever been in the intensive care nursery where Kimberly died and Tracy was treated. When I said that I had, Gary asked, "did you ever see the scales? There's a set of infant scales there that we gave. It has a little plaque on it that says, 'To the ICN, love, Kimberly.' She probably made more of an impression on the people there than I've made in 32 years of my life—in three months of hers, actually, in the last 10 days of her life. She was a fighter, even though she didn't make it.

"You know the ironic thing? The first thing they do when a baby goes in there is weigh them. And when they transferred Tracy in there, guess what scale she went on? Right. I saw the scales and broke up, fell apart. She went onto her sister's scales that we had given the ICN. Is that ironic? I just had to get out of the unit for about 10 minutes. And [the doctor who had taken care of Kimberly at the end] didn't show for like three hours. And when he came in his eyes were as red as mine."

After Kimberly died, Gary and Ginger received dozens of cards and letters of sympathy from friends and neighbors and staff members from the unit where Kimberly spent those last 10 days. There was one letter in particular, Ginger said, which she and her husband had found particularly comforting during that difficult time. She read from it: "Although some of the hurt which happened to us still lingers on, I am convinced we were all privileged to take part in a very special event which takes place once in a person's life, if that. We touched, and were touched, by a little bit of heaven, Kimberly, and we all learned a beautiful lesson, though it was a difficult one to take. That lesson was how to love and give, without reservation, although we knew we were going to put our precious selves on the line and suffer in doing so. Suffer we did, but we all learned to love, and give alot more, in a special way. . . . '

□

She is what doctors and nurses refer to when, in their darker moments, they speak among themselves of "Gorks" and "Geeks" and vegetables. She will never walk, never talk, never see, and never hear. Like Karen Ann Quinlan, she will never be aware of the extraordinary loving care she is receiving, just as, on a more basic level, she will never control her bodily functions. She spends all her days lying on her side, in a fetal position, in an oversized crib in a Washington area extended care facility. The metal bars of her crib are wrapped in foam rubber to keep her from hurting herself as she thrashes about, making guttural, animal like noises. Her medium length black hair has been pulled back into a pony tail, accentuating the fact that her head appears to be too large for her body, with its stringlike pale arms and legs. "She's been that way since she came to us five years ago. She'll always be that way," said the director of the facility, shaking his head as he walked out of the girl's room when he took me to see her two years ago. The girl is still there today. This July, she will be "sweet 16."

Three times a month, the girl is visited by her mother, a well-groomed, meticulously coiffed woman in her late forties. The woman keeps her daughter's closet filled to overflowing with brightly colored little outfits, all crisp and beautifully ironed by the woman herself. The daughter has never seen the clothes, but she wears them, and they bunch up around her waist as she squirms and thrashes in her cage of a bed. And she dribbles and drools on them as she is fed, for eating is one of the few things she can do, although she has to be fed and will never feed herself.

As the mother and I sat talking in the living room of her suburban Maryland home, she told me that her daughter had appeared to be normal at birth. "We weren't aware of anything until she was three months. She was vomiting, first thing in the morning. By the time I'd get to her it would be all over with. They put her in the hospital and determined it was probably epilepsy. They put her on medication for that and everything progressed very rapidly from there. She went into more and more convulsions until they put her in the hospital at seven months of age and determined that it was

more than just epilepsy. She was quickly going down hill. I
had the feeling she wasn't seeing because she had these little
mobile units over her crib and sometimes she'd bat at them
and other times she wouldn't. In other words, she wasn't
seeing them all the time. These things were obvious because
my other two [normal] kids would run around her when she
would be sitting in the playpen or something and she'd act
like she didn't see them or hear them. And then at other
times, she would. So at seven months of age she went in again
and they determined then that there was a nerve disease, but
they hadn't pinpointed it exactly, which one it was. And at
nine months they decided it was this Schilder's disease," an
irreversible degeneration of the nervous system for which
there is no known cure.

"How was she doing at that point," I asked.

"At nine months she had lost most of her sight. She was
losing her voice and she was losing her hearing."

"What sort of 'talking' was she doing then?"

"Well, what she had done up until she was about seven
months of age was the usual gurgling, da-da type of things.
By nine months she was losing her voice, her eyesight, her
hearing and it was not completely gone. But by a year, which
was the following July, she was completely blind, deaf, and
had no voice, made no sounds at all. Also, her neck muscles
were going, so she couldn't hold her head up. Floppy baby,
you might say. That's what they called it."

"She wasn't making any sounds?"

"No," replied the mother, "not at a year. No crying.
Nothing. And in that period of time, from the time this was
all diagnosed until she was three, I can't begin to tell you
how many times she was in and out of the hospital, and in
most cases it was pneumonia and serious. She was on the
critical list once and not expected to live."

Every time the girl was hospitalized, she would run up a
bill of about $700 to $800, said the mother, who added,

"this was in the 1960s when the hospital bills were alot lower." The family also had to keep the girl on medication. "We had her on medication every six hours around the clock, on three different drugs, and it was very expensive. Her drug bill must have run us close to $30 or $40 per month. It's really hard to remember because that's going back 12 years. I do recall a druggist said it was the highest drug bill that anybody had in the drug store for that particular year, because we went in to get an accounting for income tax purposes."

"Was she your first child," I asked.

"No, the fourth."

"And all the others are healthy and normal?"

"Right. Healthy boys. The oldest is 23, the next is 16, and the next is 15."

"So she was a fairly late baby?"

"Late in the sense that I was in my thirties when I had her," replied the girl's mother.

It is not at all uncommon in cases like the little girl's where there is absolutely no hope of improvement and the child cannot communicate with, or relate to, those around her on even the most basic of levels, to let a disease like pneumonia run its natural course. Knowing this, I was puzzled by the mother's fighting to keep the girl alive all those years. For this was not, after all, a mongoloid child, who may be severely retarded, but can certainly give and receive love, and benefit from the attention of his or her parents and siblings. And this was not an only child, upon whom two parents had built all their hopes and dreams. She was, and is, the fourth child in a family of healthy, normal children.

"Did you ever give any thought, while she was going through these bouts of pneumonia and was on the critical list, to the idea of stopping her drugs and letting her die," I asked, apologizing for the question before asking it.

"No I did not," she replied, firmly, and a bit angrily. "I'm very much opposed to it. As a matter of fact, I had a discussion with a doctor that as long as there was one breath of life in my child's body I wanted them to do all they could to save her."

"Did he suggest that?"

"The doctor was very much in favor of saving her at any cost. He asked me how I felt."

"How did the subject come up?"

"Another doctor felt that it was pointless to continue with tubes and this type of treatment and had mentioned it to the doctor who was her doctor."

"Who was the second doctor," I asked, "was he a specialist?"

"Yes, he was a specialist, who in turn mentioned it to me, and I just blew, I wanted no consideration of this type of thing."

"I hate to have to ask you these things but, why not?"

"Well, I feel there's a certain amount of love that this child is due as a normal human being gets. I think she was deprived of an awful lot, but why deprive her of the only thing in life that we can give her, which is our love? Secondly, I had three boys to raise. I feel like if I did anything to prevent that child's life, I couldn't look at my three boys, because I would have done something that had taken away from this world, and who's to know why she was put here? I have the other thing that has since turned out, I think, to prove that it was a wise decision. My boys are extremely, extremely good boys, in so far as their compassion towards other people, their helpfulness. They are fine boys. I haven't had one bit of trouble with any one of them. I attribute that to the fact that they were so involved with this child that they realized how much we had given to ourselves for that child, that they just couldn't possibly turn around and more or less give us more problems. I really, truly believe that. If anything, they will go out of their way to be helpful, and I think some of this has got to have rubbed off from the fact they've seen what we have done for their sister. And one other thing—I've never, never tried to hide her."

"It is somewhat unusual that your boys have turned out so well," I said, "because it's very common to have numerous psychological problems with other children in a family with a child like your daughter."

"I don't think so," said the girl's mother. "That did worry me, as to when the boys would begin bringing their friends here whether or not that would be an impediment to having her home. But I made up my mind that was worth the struggle. If [other children] thought this was so bad, they weren't really friends anyway."

"So you kept her at home until she was how old?"

"Eight and a half."

"Then you had to put her in an institution?"

"No, but, there was a physical problem insofar as being able to take care of her. I had lost a lot of weight, and I was, kind of, you know, declining. Nothing serious. It's just that every six hours, all around the clock, you're medicating her, doing all these things without help. We tried to get visiting nurses and what not to come in. Plus the fact that it's like a prison. You don't get out. You have no other release. You're just here all the time. My doctor felt we had to do something about getting her into a home of some kind because of my health. It was more of a, I suppose you'd say, a mental problem, a depressing problem. The first eight years of her life, we did nothing. We took the children no place. We had no vacations. We just had vast quantities of company."

"You never got more than six hours sleep, I take it."

"No, we never did."

"When I visited your daughter in the institution, I noticed all the dresses in her closet. Does that get to you?

What do you think about when you're ironing those dresses?"

"Well, I'll tell you one thing. It kind of hurts. When we were aware of her being so ill, a bed patient and everything, well, there's a heck of a lot of things you can't buy for a bed patient. And I always wanted a little girl, because my idea was, you know, really to dress up a little girl. That part hurt. It used to hurt to go into toy stores and not buy toys for her when all the other kids were going out and getting dolls and all this type of thing. That's a very, very, very hard thing to go through. It sounds trivial, but it is hard. But I guess I'm used to the idea. I know she can only have certain types of dresses, nothing with big bows in it, because being in the bed so long she has to have very straight line cut dresses. I enjoy shopping for her now. I'm over that upheaval, or that tender part of it. I can enjoy going into little girl shops and shopping for her."

"Did this ever make you question your faith in God, your religious beliefs," I asked the woman, who said she was a devout Catholic.

"I think once, that I can recall. I never got to the point where I kept questioning 'why me?' But one time I know that I was very short with a sister down at the hospital. She came in, and I think I was just getting so sick of having all these sisters and priests come in and tell me what a wonderful person I was to have this cross, this was God's cross, this type of thing. It finally got to me, you know, I just couldn't listen to any more of it. And one sister did come in and make a remark that my daughter was my stepping stone to Heaven. And I answered the sister that I couldn't care less. As far as I was concerned she would also be my stepping stone to Hell, and the sister flew out of the room. I was immediately sorry I had said it, but at that point, it was just the way I felt. I had heard so much of this drivel and patting on the back bit, that you didn't ask for, didn't want. I'm not one that can take alot of sympathy. It was just getting to me because they were always giving me that kind of stuff, preaching about the fact that God wants you to do this, and it's your cross. A little bit of that might help, but it was too much . . . I just questioned all the drivel I was getting. I didn't ever for any moment think that I shouldn't have been given, as they call it, the cross. I mean it was just my lot in life."

"Do you think God did this to you deliberately?"

"I think God just decides he's going to give you something to bear. I think that diagnostically she's a freak of nature, but I think that this was all planned."

"What have you learned from all this?"

"I certainly have learned about trouble, and how to be kind to people or help people, or overlook an awful lot of things that are wrong with people, common, ordinary things that most people get all riled up over. I just feel they're so insignificant compared to a condition like my child's, or a child like mine. It isn't a child that you want, but when you have her, you just have to love her."

"Will she be better off when she dies?"

"Oh, I think so," said the mother of the girl in the padded crib. "I think we all will be. I think she'll be quite well rewarded."

Part Five

THE WILL TO LIVE
AND THE LIVING WILL

8

I Will Not Play God!

Their stories lack the appeal of stories involving parents who must decide the fate of their horribly deformed infants. And they lack the drama and romance of the Quinlan case, for they do not involve attractive young women inexplicably turned into sleeping horrors. But every day, in hospital waiting rooms and home living rooms all over America, hundreds of families are going through much the same agony experienced by Joe and Julie Quinlan. For these mothers and fathers, sisters and brothers, husbands and wives, must face a moral and ethical dilemma nearly identical to that faced by the Quinlans and parents of horribly deformed children: they must ask, in regard to a dying loved one, should we authorize this treatment, this operation, when there is a very good chance it will only serve to hasten death? We know death is an imminent certainty without this procedure, but is the risk worthwhile? Would the patient want to take the chance, given the choice?

In these cases, as in the Quinlan case, families must consider the medical benefits and risks that are, more often than not, poorly explained or not explained at all by the treating physician. They must consider the psychological and social risks involved: Will they feel guilt ridden for years if they do not take the chance? Will they feel equally, or more guilt ridden if they do? Will they be blamed by other members of the family if they authorize an unsuccessful operation? Or will there be bitter recriminations and perhaps even a law suit if they do not "do everything possible" for the dying family member?

We never hear of these cases perhaps because they are so common. Or perhaps we never hear of them because we do not want to, because we are unable to face the fact that we could very easily find ourselves one day confronting the need to "play God" for a member of our family. Looking at such problems, however, is the only way we can ever hope to be able to handle them with some degree of comfort when our time comes to confront them.

While it is virtually impossible to imagine ourselves going through Joe and Julie Quinlan's personal Hell—for how many of us has ever known someone who in the prime of life, slipped into a coma and never recovered—it is very easy to identify with the family of Stanley Levey. For Stanley Levey was a victim of heart disease, and that is something we can understand, or at least fear, for it kills more of us than any other natural cause.

□

It was 1:00 A.M. An hour for dreaming, if asleep, soul searching, if awake. Robert Levey, Stan Levey's oldest son, sat leaning forward, on the edge of the sofa, his large frame folded, arms resting on knees. He spoke softly, pausing frequently to consider carefully the questions I asked him. He said he did not mind discussing the decisions he had to help make some three years earlier for his critically ill father. But the longer he talked, the less happy he seemed to be giving a guided tour of the graveyard of his soul.

Bob and his father had always been quite close and remained so through Stan's divorce and remarriage. Both father and son were physically active men. Bob was addicted to pickup basketball and touch football games; his father always had "a thing about physical conditioning." Both men were journalists; Stanley Levey was a Scripps Howard's labor editor; his son was an assistant city editor for *The Washington Post*. Bob's entering his father's profession was a fact in part brought about by, and in part contributing to, their closeness.

As we sat talking in the dimly lit room, Bob remembered a night when he had sat in a similarily darkened jet liner hurtling eastward across the North Atlantic to his father, who lay in a Turkish hospital, the victim of a debilitating heart attack. "Well, there I was, over Weathership Charlie, over the Atlantic, trying to get ready for I didn't know what. I sort of replayed all the years, and there weren't that many. I wasn't too old then, about 25. Barely. I half expected to be told he was dead when I got there. The shock of the telegram. And the shock of the moment. And then having all night on that God damn airplane trying to think about it."

Stanley Levey, in the fifty-sixth year of his life, had been vacationing in Turkey with his wife, Nan, when he had been stricken by a massive heart attack. It was an attack so massive, in fact, that his family was later told he should not have survived it. For about seven weeks Nan coped with the situation of being thousands of miles from home, in a strange land with an alien culture, attempting to deal with a husband near death and virtually no one who spoke any English. "She had about had it," remembered Bob, "and I realized within a day of arriving that the purpose of the telegram was to say 'come bail me out.' "

Bob said that his stepmother, with whom he got along very well, had prepared him for how sick his father was. "But still, I will never forget walking into his room. I did not know what to expect, even though Nan could not have made it clearer, even though she made it as clear as possible. You know, the first thing that struck me was how thin he was," having lost 40 pounds in the seven weeks. "There was no brain damage but very big physical weakness, you know. Sitting in a chair would exhaust him. He was up within a week [of the attack], but walking the five steps from the chair to get back in bed would tire him out for 20 minutes.

"The decision at that point," Bob remembered, "was, was he strong enough to be moved, and the doctors didn't feel he was. You know, if walking four steps was going to do him in, you know a jet flight to the U.S. was going to destroy him. So we had to wait until he could get strong enough to be able to handle a little flight, little in this case being several hours to an Air Force hospital in Germany. It was about two weeks before we could do it.

"In Germany, they were able to put him on a special diet with various exercise machines and that kind of thing. He really did improve. It was remarkable, but really the point of Germany was just to get him in enough shape to handle that jet trip home, which, of course, is hard enough ... " Bob's voice trailed off, as it did frequently during our conversation.

"What was the prognosis at that point," I asked.

"That it could go any way at all. He could make a complete recovery, although that was doubtful. Probably the best he could hope for at that point was limited kind of work where he'd work maybe three, four hours max, with long rests. But for a guy who's worked flat out his whole life that was the same thing as saying, 'Retire.' But he didn't seem to mind that. It was funny, but he saw it as the chance to write 'the book,' and to take it easy, you know."

"So he was looking forward to being forced into an early retirement?"

"Exactly. But of course there was a gloomier side. I got to be friends with this male nurse at the Air Force hospital, and over a beer one night I asked him what prognosis really was. He said it was terrible. He said he'd never seen a guy as sick who had lived as long. But who knows, you know? You live from day to day. You'd watch him and you'd see an improvement. There was no particularly upsetting incident. He didn't black out. No blue face. No red face. He was much better able to sit in chairs, and he was doing some walking."

"And he was mentally alert?"

"Oh, yeah. He was in Germany about a week and he was making progress. And then comes the flight back. It was an Air Force hospital plane with all the walking wounded. What a show that was. It makes a weekly round trip from some base in New Jersey, McGuire, I think. It goes all through Europe, down into Africa and back through Europe, picking up all the seriously ill or injured Americans. So there we are, over the Atlantic, in this tin can with no windows. We've got one guy who fell off an Alp, another guy who was in a car accident in Ethiopia. It was insane. Agony."

"How was he taking it all?"

"He was bad but stable. He was still awake and could move around a little. We did crossword puzzles and things. He was alert as hell. We even had a little talk. He was depressed—noticeably."

"Was he talking about dying?"

"No, not at all. He was talking like, you know, Chamber of Commerce booster stuff: 'I'm going to read this; I'm going to do that; I'm going to go right on as I did before.' There was some chance of that if you believed the doctors."

When the family arrived back in the United States, Stanley Levey was admitted to George Washington University Medical Center, in Washington, D.C., "where they put him in therapy. Again, more exercise machines. And he was much, much improved. He could walk down the hall, very haltingly,

but he could do it. We were really thinking about the
prospect of him leading a fairly limited, but reasonably solid,
life. He went home from the hospital in early October. This
would be four months after the heart attack. And he came
over for Thanksgiving," remembered Bob, "and he seemed in
pretty good shape."

Bob was out of the country for about a month after
that Thanksgiving, and "when we came back, the change was
obvious. He was much weaker and much more depressed."

"Depressed by what? His limitations?"

"By his limitations, exactly right. And it was still not a
life or death situation by any means. He could still function.
Nan was back at work and didn't have to look after him
every minute," and her mother was there to care for Stan.

"And he still wasn't talking about his condition, about
what was depressing him?"

"No, he was talking about next year's vacation, for
God's sake! And I remember having the sense of how absurd
that was to discuss . . . . "

"But you didn't tell him that?"

"No. I didn't say it. I didn't bring it up."

"Did he just get weaker and weaker," I asked Bob.

"Weaker and weaker, until finally he was driving Nan
bananas. He couldn't ever sleep, and he was having pains in
his knees, caused by bad circulation. He was also acting
forgetful and was occasionally irrational."

So once again in mid-February 1971, Stanley Levey
returned to the hospital. His condition, as his eldest son
remembered it three years later, was "good but weak. They
ran a new battery of tests with a new consultant, and finally,
for the first time, we got a good line on what the hell was
wrong with him—what the hell was wrong with him was that
his heart was just not doing anything. It was maybe working
at one third of its capacity. The doctor broke down at one
point a little bit, you know, weakened his front, and said 'I

do not understand how this man is here alive.' Well, now that started putting a different cast on things. The doctor said he could die tomorrow. He could die in an hour. He could die in 10 years. He said his guess would be that we're talking about somebody who probably would not live another couple of months."

The doctors decided to do an angiogram at that point. The test, which involves injecting an opaque fluid into an artery in order to watch it as it moves through the heart, revealed that 40 percent of Stanley Levey's heart was nothing but scar tissue. And the 60 percent which wasn't scar tissue was badly weakened and unable to provide proper circulation of the blood. By that time, recalled Bob, the family had some decisions to make.

"Now it was February, and the doctors weren't liking what they were seeing at all. He was beginning to get a little disoriented and his heart was failing. He called me John and my brother Rob, that kind of stuff. But then at other times he'd be very lucid, and it was obvious that what was happening was that his brain was working fine sometimes and not so fine at others from oxygen starvation. And just very gradually, he was sinking," said Bob quietly.

There was one episode Bob recalled as being particularly painful. A group of Stan's friends had taken time off from work to visit him in the hospital, and, "I was just leaving when they were coming down the hall. There were three of them, and they were going to go in there and kind of try the drunk sailor approach. They walked in and said 'how are you,' and 'the nurse has great legs, doesn't she,' and that kind of stuff. But he was in his own little world. He was in one of his down phases, and he just said, 'Oh, why are you here?' He knew them, but he didn't understand why they had come to see him. And they, they just left. There were still moments when he was together, but there were many more when he wasn't. And finally, the decision.

"It had happened pretty quickly over the course of three weeks," said Bob, who was beginning to look as though the lateness of the hour and painfulness of the discussion were starting to wear on him. "He changed from an entirely lucid person to a mostly unlucid one. He was senile. He was blabbering. He couldn't stay on a point, flashing from the past to the present to the future to the present. He didn't know who was in the room with him. He'd do things like get out of bed, putting his bathrobe on, and the nurse would say, 'That's good that you put on your bathrobe,' almost as if he was a two-year-old. And he'd say, 'where's my bathrobe?' And it was on him, for Christ sake!"

"So at that point . . . "

"At that point, the doctors came and we had a huddle. They said, 'Listen, you know this man is surely dying. Sure as hell, as we told you before, it's a miracle he's lived this long.' This was now, what the hell could it be?" Bob paused, leaning back on the sofa as he attempted to recall past events best left in the past. "It was a little more than eight months after the attack. And they said there are two clear cut choices: One was to let him coast out, in which case the same numbers—he could die in an hour, a day, a year."

"When you say 'coast out,' were you talking about putting him on machines, when the time came, or just letting him die naturally?"

"Let him go as slowly and easily as possible," said Bob, who had been lucky enough never to have heard any other possibility discussed. But there was, as he had said, a second choice.

"The other option was open heart surgery. The point of that would be to correct an aneurism in the heart—a defect which causes a portion of the wall to balloon out—and repair a deteriorated valve. They felt that if they could replace the valve there would be a good chance for what they called a 'limited life.' I will never forget that phrase—a 'limited life.' "

"Were they assuming at that point that the lack of oxygen had caused permanent brain damage," I asked.

"There would be if they didn't move fast."

"But they didn't think there had been any yet?"

"They were sure there hadn't been. But they said, 'We cannot screw around with this. We've got to do it and we've got to do it very soon.'"

"How much time did they give you?"

"Two weeks. Well, two weeks to hit surgery. Much less to decide. They said, and this was on a Friday, they said 'we absolutely have to have a decision by Monday.'"

"What were the odds of his pulling through?"

"Three to one against survival," said Bob, recalling the odds with the assurance of a Las Vegas casino owner quoting the risk to the house.

"So those were the choices. And I remember asking at that time, and this was about 11 days before surgery, 'what does a "limited life" mean?' And they, knowing what he did for a living, said, 'well, it's probably going to mean a fairly monastic, scholarly sort of life at home. It's going to mean never getting tired. It's going to mean no traveling out in the boondocks, away from the beaten path and so on. It's going to mean taking it pretty easy.'"

"But he could still write his book?"

"Sure he could write the book, but he couldn't go all over town for interviews in a day. No way."

"So he'd be functioning as an older person?"

"Exactly. He would be [like] a 75-year-old."

"Was he given any choice at all?"

"He wasn't told a thing," remembered Bob.

"It was all on you," I asked.

"It was all on me, John, and Nan."

Physicians are often accused of precluding family members from making decisions regarding the fate of critically ill relatives, and they are often so accused with very good reason. The doctrine of informed consent, which governs all patient/physician relations, holds that the patient, or person responsible for the patient, must be fully informed of, and completely understand, the treatment proposed by the doctor before giving approval for that treatment to begin. In practice, however, the doctrine is often virtually abandoned. The patient, or family member, is told only in the most general terms what the situation is, and the patient or family member is often presented with the options in such a way as to make only one choice possible—the choice already made by the doctor.

Bob Levey, his brother, and stepmother were left on their own to reach their decision. As Bob remembered the situation from the distance of three years, the doctors simply presented the facts, explained the situation medically, and then left the family on its own. The Leveys were not given any ambiguous advice which they might fall back on in later years, when, in the dark of night, they questioned the wisdom of their choice.

"What did the three of you do," I asked. "What did you think of the options?"

"We had the most ferocious 12-hour argument you can possibly imagine," said Bob. "It was a real horror show."

"Who wanted . . . . '

"They wanted the operation immediately and I didn't."

"Why didn't you want it?"

"I didn't like the odds. I had an aesthetic feeling about it. It wasn't a medical thing, but an aesthetic feeling, about carving somebody up, and it just made me sick when I thought about it."

"You mean, you figured that if the odds were against him anyway, you'd rather just let him go naturally?"

"That's it, just let him down gently."

"You didn't think about the idea of not putting him on a respirator when and if the time came for that?"

"I didn't think that far ahead. I had not thought through the fact that somebody could just be technically . . . . "

"Kept alive indefinitely? Technically alive?"

"I remember thinking that if, you know, if we let him coast out I thought that what would happen is that one morning he would just be gone, respirator or no respirator, he would just cave in. And it was a very bitter scene."

"What did John and Nan argue?"

"They said 'we've got to do everything we can to save him right now. The doctors said act quickly. The doctors said you're risking permanent brain damage. You're going to risk making him a worse God damn vegetable.' And I said, 'I know all that, but the man's obviously had it!'"

"They felt you should take the chance of bringing him back even though he would probably die in the attempt?"

"Right. They wanted all or nothing. Push all your chips out into the center of the table kind of move. And I remember standing in the middle of the living room saying, 'Look, I'm not God, and I'm not going to do this! I will not make a decision!' Even though it meant certain death."

"Were they thinking that he'd survive the operation even though the odds were three to one against his coming through?"

"Sure. They were hoping he would. Of course those aren't the longest odds in the world. They're not ten to one. We were still dealing with what we hoped was more than half a functioning human heart."

"Who had the legal right to make the decision," I asked Bob.

"Nan," he replied, his tone of voice three years later was one of resignation and acceptance rather than one reflecting the bitterness he said he felt that difficult night.

"How did they win you over? "

"Because it was so obvious that it was the only thing to do. And who knows? I'm a gambler. It was a chance against a sure thing."

"Did Nan and John have different reasons for arriving at the same decision?"

"No, their reasons were essentially the same: 'You take the only chance.' . . . They thought it was an easy question. I remember being irritated as hell at that."

"In other words, they thought there was no choice?"

"There was no choice, of course. You take the only option for survival and . . . . "

"You mention that your sense of aesthetics was offended by what would happen in the operating room. But as a gambler, why didn't you want to take the chance of winning the 'biggest hand'?"

"I can't really say. I guess it was because I was . . . I don't know," Bob said, looking, for the first time during the lengthly conversation, genuinely perplexed. "He had had so much of hospitals in his time, so much of them. As a young kid, with rheumatic fever, he missed a year of school. He washed out of the service because of illness, went to Mississippi in the 1940s and he blew it, got hepatitis. Bingo. Goodbye. We don't need you. He got hepatitis again when I was a little boy in the 1950s, laid up for months. He had always had such a thing about his age, lying it down, and such a big thing about physical conditioning. I was making a purely aesthetic objection in the face of the only chance."

"You felt that he wouldn't want to live with the limitations which would be imposed on him?"

"Yeah, I did feel that way. And he hadn't been handling the limitations well in all those months before he went back into the hospital. He had had terrific depression. He was impossible to be around."

"Had he ever spoken of suicide?"

"Never. Quite the opposite, he said 'I can't stand it this way but I'm going to try to make it.' But he never made it emotionally. He was having a terrible time."

"So he wanted to make it but obviously couldn't adjust to his limitations? Did that figure in your thinking?"

"Very much. I just saw that . . . I didn't go for that self-serving 'this is the way he would have wanted it' business, because to this day I'm not sure how he would have gone. But there was no question of asking him, because he wouldn't have understood. I felt that in terms of pain, there was no choice to make, because obviously he'd be under anesthesia in surgery. And without surgery he had some pain, but nothing tremendous. But I was trying to see the whole life pattern, and the whole life pattern didn't include dying with your chest in two halves and your rib cage opened up like that and men in white coats standing all around you."

"Why were the 12 hours of discussion bitter and nasty?"

"Mostly because my brother and I got off on a tangent about me attacking Nan, saying, 'why do you have the right to make this decision?' I felt very strongly about the birth right—that my brother and I should make the decision."

"Would you have felt the same way were your natural mother involved in the situation?"

"No, but I felt that 'the torch passes, and this should be our decision that we will live with,' and Nan felt the same way from her point of view," said Bob, who had been, and remains to this day, very close to his stepmother.

"Did your brother feel as you did?"

"Yes, but he disagreed with me on the decision. He definitely felt that Nan shouldn't make the decision. He felt that none of us should make it. He felt at first that the doctor should decide, the guy who was going to be the chief surgeon. I got all over him for copping out, and flew the 'torch passes' idea at him. He bought that, but then he said, 'well, there's no choice, is there? You have to shoot for some chance of survival, even in the face of three to one odds.' It was a swell evening."

"What was Nan's logic?"

"Her line was, 'I'm his wife,' you know. 'It's a much different relationship. I've been with him since the beginning of this thing. I've lived it. I've agonized over it and he's my husband. You at least have your wives. Your younger, but this is my life.' So it was quite a night. It began after dinner and ended around dawn."

"Where there tears?"

"Oh, sure. Not by me though, I remember that. It was her all the way. My brother was a little horrified by it all."

"By her crying?"

"Yeah. I mean, after we got past the question of who was going to make the decision, and that was essentially resolved by saying we'd all make it; it would be a majority vote. And then my brother said, 'What the hell else do we have to discuss?' This was in about the third hour and he said, 'we obviously go for surgery.' He saw it in a very simple way. You know, betting possible death against certain death. He argued that Dad would want any kind of shot at meaningful life."

"Did you discuss what constitutes a meaningful life?"

"Yes, we did. We even got into sex, as a matter of fact, which is something my father had gotten into with me privately months earlier. It really upset the hell out of him [that he would have to give up sex]. I remember that very well. But she said she was willing to live without it if she could have him."

"Would he be an invalid?"

"An extremely limited person, physically. And he'd still have periods of mentally floating in and out," which indicates, regardless of what Bob remembered being told, Stan Levey had already suffered some permanent brain damage.

The problem "was never spelled out," Bob said, "but that was the impression I got, that there was not going to be any substantial improvement over [his preoperative state] and the best that could be hoped for was that he wouldn't deteriorate."

"How did the doctors handle all this?"

"They handled it well. They were very aware of the human relationships involved. We got into a situation where the nurses were interested in this case, and so were the doctors, especially after they heard the whole Turkey story. It does sound like a melodrama, really. I think now, and this is just a private fantasy I have, that the reason they got interested was because this guy had no 'right' to be alive after what he'd gone through. He was a miracle, and they really wanted to see why he had lived for eight months after a fantastic heart attack."

"So by dawn [of the night of the argument] you gave in?"

"Not feeling good about it. Thinking, fantasizing ahead about surgery. What would it be like? What would I feel like? I felt that day, 11 days before surgery, that I was sure he was going to die. It was like a countdown where you were quite sure what was going to happen. It was really weird. I'll tell you, I felt more like a life-taker by sitting around for 11 days, as though I had a ticket in my pocket which said '3 to 1 against,' than I ever would have felt by just letting him go. But one thing I ought to stress, is that I may, in a way, have been ducking my responsibility. I think it would have been a lot easier for me to live with my original feelings on it; just let him down easy. It would have been one of those, 'Oh well, it's out of our hands' things."

"Do you think now you should have agreed earlier to go ahead with the surgery?"

"Yes. But I'm not sure I wanted to face it then."

Bob's premonitions about surgery were correct. His

father died on the operating table. I wondered, therefore, if he initially felt he had copped out by agreeing to the surgery rather than feeling, as he did when we spoke, that he had tried to dodge his responsibilities by resisting it.

"I didn't feel that way," he responded, "because [his dying] only proved that I was right, if I wanted to look at it that way, that surgery was as much of a sure death option than no surgery. So if I wanted to protect myself, I would have said, 'well, hell, they're both no-win positions,' you know? We took the 3-to-1 gamble and it didn't work."

"But you didn't . . ."

"No, I didn't feel better. But during the operation we'd begun to have doubts about the doctors. That's a weird one. You begin to think . . . there you are, camped in the God damn waiting area in the hospital, and you've been there since seven o'clock in the morning and there's no word, no word, no word, and you . . . your mind is going, 'what's going on in there?' And then, after five hours, when you know the operation was targeted for six hours, you're thinking, 'well is he dead at this minute? Will he be dead in two minutes? When am I going to know?' Really, the uncertainty is impossible."

"But you feel now that it was something which had to be done?"

"No question about it. [Operating] was the right decision."

"What would you want done if you were in your father's place?"

"That's a good question. With exactly the same odds?"

"Right. If surgery meant a chance for a limited life, perhaps to write a book, and the other option was certain death."

"I'd take the surgery. Always," said Bob, without a moment's hesitation.

"But that's not what you wanted for your father."

"No. That's funny, isn't it? You're making me realize

something here. I don't feel like a murderer, and I don't
really feel that my original position was wrong, although I see
now it was not a reasonable thing to argue. It just wasn't.
From his position, or even from mine."

"But that was something you couldn't see at the time?"

"You definitely can't see it at the time. You really
can't. And I was, you know, arguing it the way a book ought
to end, rather than arguing it on the basis of a human being's
life. I wanted the ending to be as painless and as neat and to
wrap up as many loose ends and be as 'off into the sunset' as
possible, rather than . . . , " He paused, "Something grated on
me about taking wild gambles with someone's life, even
though the alternative was certain death. I really ought to
examine that I guess. It just seemed wild. The decision to
operate just seemed cockeyed to me. It was a fantastic
chance."

□

Three years after the death of his father, reliving the
agony through a lengthy late night discussion, Bob Levey
remembered his decision as a difficult one. And it was
difficult, for him. Just as Joseph and Julia Quinlan's decision
was a difficult one for them to make. Would Stanley Levey
have wanted to live as an invalid? Perhaps. But to ask that
question, one must ask a second question: Would Stanley
Levey have wanted to end his days as a human vegetable, as
an extension of a machine? The decision was difficult one for
Bob, John, and Nan Levey because it involved a strong,
complex, primal relationship. For most physicians, the decision would have been an easy one: Take the chance. Take the
long shot at life rather than the certainty of death. It was a
new situation for the Leveys, as it was for the Quinlans and it
almost always is for family members. But for physicians, in
this age of eternal life, the question is not, "do we take the
long shot?" Rather, the question is:"If we suceed, then what?"

9

Can't They Stop and Let Him Die?

To My Family, My Physician, My Lawyer, My Clergyman, To Any Medical Facility In Whose Care I Happen To Be, To Any Individual Who May Become Responsible For My Health, Welfare or Affairs:

Death is as much a reality as birth, growth, maturity, and old age—it is the one certainty of life. If the time comes when I,_____ , can no longer take part in decisions for my own future, let this statement stand as an expression of my wishes while I am still of sound mind.

If the situation should arise in which there is no reasonable expectation of my recovery from physical or mental disability, I request that I be allowed to die and not be kept alive by artificial or "heroic measures." I do not fear death itself as much as the indignities of deterioration, dependence, and hopeless pain. I, therefore, ask that medication be mercifully administered to me to alleviate suffering even though this may hasten the moment of death.

This request is made after careful consideration. I hope you who care for me will feel morally bound to follow its mandate. I recognize that this appears to place a heavy responsibility upon you, but it is with the intention of relieving you of such

159

responsibility and placing it upon myself in accordance with my strong convictions, that this statement is made.

Text of the Living Will distributed by the Euthanasia Educational Council

The text of the Living Will that has been distrubuted upon request to some 1.3 million Americans says volumes more about our worship of youth, beauty, and perfection, and our fear and loathing of aging, ugliness, inconvenience, and pain than it does about our problems in dealing with a medical technology which has developed faster than social morality. While many of those requesting copies of the document clearly fear that they might suffer the fate of a Karen Ann Quinlan—the council mailed out about 750,000 copies of the Will between 1969 and the first hearing in the Quinlan case, and has filled requests for almost 600,000 copies in the nine months since the trial—it is unclear from reading the will what the author had in mind. For the document, which is not yet legally binding in any state, is frighteningly vague. It does *not* request that its maker simply be allowed to die "with dignity" when death becomes inevitable. It does *not* request that its maker not be sustained should he or she become comatose or completely paralyzed. Instead, were it made legally binding (and there have been legislative proposals to make it so binding in eight states), the Will would authorize the *murder* of virtually anyone who filled out a Will, lost consciousness for a period of time, and would be in some way incapacitated upon regaining consciousness. What, for example, is meant by the words "physical or mental disability"? What is meant by "artificial means"? A person who suffers a stroke loses consciousness for a few days, and then regains consciousness and recovers to walk with a limp could be said to suffer from a "physical disability." The stroke victim who recovers but suffers from amnesia or short periods of senility is certainly suffering from a "mental disability." Obviously, one might argue, that is not what the Living Will *means*. Perhaps not. But that is what it *says*. And what is meant by the words "deterioration" and "dependence"? The person who is confined by accident or illness to a wheelchair, although he may be perfectly normal in every other respect, may certainly be said to be dependent upon others. And the person who suffers a partial loss of sight or vision may certainly be said to suffer from "deterioration." But are these candidates for what is clearly euthanasia, mercy killing? They might not think they are, but if they have filled out Living Wills, and those Living Wills become legally binding, such persons are completely at the mercy of whomever "may become responsible for [their] health, welfare or affairs."

☐

It was a miracle that Stanley Levey, whose story was told in an earlier chapter, survived the massive heart attack he suffered while vacationing overseas. It took seven weeks of bed rest before he was even up to traveling a few hours by plane to a hospital in Europe where he could be readied for the trip back to the United States. A physically active man, Stan Levey was told he would never again by physically active. He would have to give up his work, which was his life. He would, a man in his early fifties, have to lead the life of a man in his seventies. And yet he spoke incessantly of the future, not of a wish to die. While he had great trouble coping with both his physical and mental limitations and disabilities, he did strive to cope with them.

Had Stanley Levey signed a Living Will, his family would have been perfectly justified in allowing his death, in not doing everything they did to see that he had the best possible shot at survival. For Stan was a man whom, in his son's words, had a "thing about physical fitness," a man who had had "so much of hospitals in his life." How simple then, to tell oneself that death would be his first choice, given his very limited range of choices.

But there was no Living Will in the Levey case. Stan's wife and sons did all that could be done. And he lived for more than six months after the heart attack and spent a good part of that time at home. So he and his family had months together they would not have had, said things to each other which might never have been said, and his wife and son have memories of which they would have been deprived—if Stanley Levey had had a Living Will.

☐

Susan Ward was living with her husband in Providence, R.I., studying for a master's degree at Brown University when her 62-year-old mother suffered her first stroke. "She and my father had been planning a trip to Scotland and had been putting it off for a long time," Susan told me. "But they were finally getting ready to take it. They had been shopping all day at a local shopping center [in suburban Illinois] and had been buying things for their trip. They had come home, had dinner, and were watching TV when all of a the sudden my mother said to my father, 'I have the most terrible headache,' and she leaned way over. She had become partially paralyzed, although she didn't loose consciousness right away.

"Obviously it was serious," Susan continued, "and my father called an ambulance and she was taken to the hospital. I called the next day because it was her birthday, and my father had just returned from the hospital. It was 24 hours after the stroke and she was on I.V.s and couldn't recognize my father or brother. The doctor said he'd wait a day or two to assess the damage, and she was conscious when I got out there the next morning and she could recognize me. She could stammer, and that was about it. And for the first three or four nights she was out of it, and her breathing sounded really labored. But by the time she went home from the hospital the doctor called her almost completely recovered. Her speech wasn't normal, that was the only thing that wasn't normal. She could walk down the stairs with the aid of a nurse, and she could walk around. The stroke was on her right side, and she regained the use of her right leg, and her arm was coming along."

Susan said that one of the things which particularly struck her about her mother's illness was the fact that her mother said she did not remember what some would term the "indignity" of being stuck with tubes and needles. "Right before I had come back home [to Rhode Island], she had been upset about something, but I wasn't sure what it was. She had been crying and I had been crying, and she seemed to want to go home. I had assured her that if there wasn't any hope, we wouldn't leave her to die in the hospital." But when Susan returned to Illinois for a second visit, and her mother was home from the hospital, "I bugged her about what she remembered about the first week. I asked her if she remembered being in the hospital with tubes in her, and she didn't remember much. But she had a clear understanding of other things. I asked her if she was in pain or uncomfortable, and she just had a general impression of fuzziness."

One month after her first stroke, Susan Ward's mother had a second, more serious stroke. She was comatose for almost three weeks, and the doctors told her family there was little hope that she'd ever regain consciousness. But the doctors were wrong. As of this writing Susan's mother "seems to recognize people," although she has not yet regained her speech. And once again, she seems to be heading home, although her prospects are not as bright at this point.

But had Susan's mother had a Living Will, her family and physicians might not have pulled her through the first stroke. She would not have been "subjected" to the "indignity" of having I.V.s attached to her body. And she might well have died in the first few days. Had that happened, Susan, her mother, father and brother would have been deprived of that unique month. It was a difficult month, but it was a special month. For although Susan and her mother have always been very close, it was a time of intense closeness, a time when Susan, no longer a little girl, could, as a woman, share with her mother and help her mother to recover much in the same way Susan's mother had helped her as she matured from little girl to grown woman. It was something they would not have shared had Susan's mother feared "the indignities of deterioration, dependence and hopeless measures."

□

"I think that writing wills will make the problem worse, not better," Andre Hellegers told me. Dr. Hellegers, the director of the Kennedy Institute for the Study of Human Reproduction and Bioethics, went on to say "It is useless to write a will which cannot be enforced, so one has to think who is going to sue whom for what. Presumably a doctor would be sued for treating a person who had a Will against his will." Such a situation, said Dr. Hellegers, could create a climate in which "doctors will stay away from those who have such a will.... " It is, he said, also "extremely dangerous, because it acknowledges that doctors have a right of ownership unless you write a will. I would be afraid that the person who doesn't have a will would be presumed to be the doctor's property, and there would also be cases where those who did have it wouldn't be resuscitated" when they should be.

"What would happen," the doctor asked, "if Joe had a Will, and Joe was in a coma, and the family said, 'I talked to Joe yesterday and he said he wanted to change the Will?' . . . It drives a further wedge between individuals and families and creates a superclass—physicians . . . . What are demanded right now [rather than Living Wills] are a few lawsuits against physicians who persist in battering patients, in doctors giving dying patients useless treatment. Patients do *not* belong to doctors. Doctors have no right of ownership. Consequently, doctors have no right to treat a patient against his will."

Like many of the older physicians who told me they have withheld treatment from dying patients, Dr. Hellegers, an obstetrician-gynocologist, had a personal story to tell. "My grandfather was a surgeon in Belgium. He developed cancer of the rectum and was told that if he had a colostomy, he could last a long time. But he said, 'Hell, I wouldn't want to live that way, it'll just delay my dying!' He told his doctor, 'go see my family, explain the situation to them. If they see any point for me to be around, I'll suffer it.' " Although the senior Dr. Helleger's family saw enormous point in his being "around," they did not see why he should suffer, and he passed up the surgery.

In some ways, Andre Hellegers told me, "it may be less acceptable today to cease useless treatment than it was in the past. Once' people believed there was a life hereafter, so they were willing to accept death as a standard procedure. Today, my God, you don't allow a child to see a dead person for fear they may think they themselves will die some day. Death is dumped on the hospitals, away from the home, sterile." Death is indeed dumped on the hospitals. Around the turn of the century, about 90 percent of those who died in bed, died at home. Today, more than 80 percent of us die in institutions, and death is something hidden away in the back rooms of our hospitals, nursing homes, and other institutions for the care

and storage of the aged and infirm. We seem to think that if
we refuse to acknowledge and see death, we can avoid it. It
would be bad enough if this attitude were confined to the lay
public alone, but it is not. It is equally prevalent among
health professionals, the doctors and nurses who see to it that
their dying patients are always placed in the rooms farthest
from the nursing station, who never seem to have a moment
to spend with the dying, and who, in many cases, refuse to
admit to the patient that he or she is, in fact, dying.

□

It was the final day of classes for the year, and as the
students filed into the medical school lecture hall, many were
wearing shorts and T-shirts, and most laughed and chattered
about plans for the up-coming summer vacation. They
quieted a bit, but not much, as the instructor explained that
they were about to see a video tape, made a local medical
center, of a woman who had made the decision to leave renal
dialysis. The lights were turned out, the projector was turned
on, and the image of a woman in her seventies, lying in a
hospital bed, appeared on the screen. The sound in the
lecture hall was bad, and one had to strain to hear the woman
in the film as she explained that she would rather die than
continue to depend on the kidney machine to live. At first,
her voice was the only sound in the hall. But then, "Pop!
Pop! Pop—Pop—Pop!" Singly, at first, and then in bursts all
over the darkened room came the sound of soda and beer
cans being opened. The popping of can tops quickly blended
with laughter and chatter as cans were passed around the
room. The hall full of future physicians began to party in the
dark as a long-dead woman's gift to them, the video tape in
which she reveald her inner most feelings and fears, was
projected on the screen. And what will those doctors say
when first asked by a patient, "Doctor, should I go on the

machine? Is it worth it? What have other patients told you? Help me, doctor."

□

While there is much talk by healthy intellectuals about Living Wills and "death with dignity," it must be noted that there is far less such talk among the dying. Physicians to whom I have spoken, including those who deal with cancer patients day in and day out, have universally expressed the opinion that the vast majority of their patients want to live any way they can, rather than "die with dignity."

"How often do you have patients who say they want to stop their treatments," I asked a radiation therapist who asked me that I not use his name.

"Almost never," he replied. "I have a feeling that this is vastly over stated. Most people want to live and this is an instinct which is pretty strong. I don't think [patient attitudes toward dying and death] are any different now than they were ten years ago."

Dr. John Potter, a surgical oncologist [specialist in the surgical treatment of cancer] told me he sees patients who want to die "about once a year, at the most. Where the situation comes up more frequently is that patient with advanced cancer who needs support to live, is vomiting, in pain, bleeding—where there is no hope of any cure. You can maintain his life by putting tubes down his nose, by giving him blood. But that is not prolonging life; that's delaying death. Those are heroic means, and I don't believe they are required. Putting it more strongly, I don't think it should be done. I don't believe in euthanasia, that's a moral wrong. But I don't believe in prolonging life when there's nothing I can do to cure the patient."

"For 25 years, I've been in this specialty," said Dr. Charles Rath, a hemotologist. "All the patients I've seen have been for hematology—leukemia, Hodgkin's—I can only think of four or five patients who have said to me, 'Dr. Rath, I want to die. Why don't you let me die?" I have had about two patients who have committed suicide because of their disease." Because he has had so few patients who wanted to die, Dr. Rath told me that he remembers well those who wished to do so. "One I remember very well was a lawyer, a wonderful person, who was about seventy. He wasn't practicing anymore, and he knew he had a disease that was incureable. When he came to see me he was just letting me study his case. One of the attractions of being a doctor is to show that you can do better than anyone else," said Charles Rath, almost as an aside. "After I had run all sorts of tests and studied his case thoroughly, he said, 'I know you had to do that to satisify yourself. But I'd like to die. My wife is right here, [and was in Dr. Rath's office at that moment] and she knows I want to die. The one thing I can't stand is pain.' But [even then], I couldn't let him die without doing the simple things until he was in a coma. Once he was in a coma, I let him go," said Dr. Rath. "As a matter of fact, if I have a patient I've worked closely with and I know I've made repeated attempts to make them better and can't do any more, once they've lost consciousness, I let them go. I wouldn't stop oxygen or I.V.s, but I wouldn't revive them. I get angry when I see somebody doing that, although I wouldn't say so. I don't discuss it with a patient, but my own philosophy is I don't want to revive anybody with a fatal disease if it's in a terminal stage.

"It's the older doctors who feel as I do," Dr. Rath told me. "The younger ones generally want to continue. They don't have a full picture of the disease, just what they see in the hospital. You're influenced by your own experiences. The quality of life is very important. I've had patients who wanted to be kept alive, whose quality of life was so poor, and the impact of their disease was so great on their families, that I've felt ashamed of myself for keeping them alive." But it all comes down to a question of "who is the doctor responsible to," Charles Rath said. "Who is he working for? Is it the patient or the family? My feeling is that my primary responsibility is to the patient, to do what he tells me and what he wants. Sometimes the family comes in and tries to control the situation. They say, 'we don't want you to tell him what he's got.' "

It would be easy to write off the observations of these physicians by saying they are simply presenting the bright side and are not listening carefully to their dying patients were it not possible to back up their observations with statistics. In 1974, there were 25,683 suicides, which means that about one percent of the Americans who died that year died by their own hand. That same year, 360,472 persons died of cancer. That means that even if every one of the 25,683 persons who killed themselves did so because they were suffering the ravages of cancer, only about 7 percent of the cancer patients would have killed themselves. While it is virtually impossible to discover what percentage of patients with terminal illnesses do chose to cheat their disease, one study of the psychological problems of kidney patients states that patients whose lives depend upon the kidney machine commit suicide at about 400 times the national rate. Yet even that estimate, which many experts believe is extremely high, translates to the fact that only 4.8 percent of those persons who live as an appendage of a machine chose to kill themselves.

But none of this is to suggest that the way we treat our dying and elderly populations is something of which we ought to be proud. All that is suggested here is that we have in some perverse way become so enthralled with the idea of dying—perhaps because death has for so many years shared our psychic closet with that other major taboo subject, sex—that we assume that everyone who is nearing death wants to reach it in a hurry. Nothing could be farther from the truth.

"A great many older people are surprisingly tenacious in their attempts to hang on to life," Dr. Robert N. Butler told me. Dr. Butler is director of the recently established National Institute on Aging and author of *Why Survive? Being Old in America*, the 1976 winner of the Pulitzer Prize for general nonfiction. He went on to add, however, that "one quarter of all suicides occur among folks over sixty-five." Like most of the other physicians to whom I have spoken, Dr. Butler, a psychiatrist, said it is rare to have a patient ask to die. But he told me he had had one such patient who came to him for a mental examination. The man was older, but not elderly, and was facing "an illness which would leave him helpless and his family in great debt." The man intended to commit suicide, had tape recorded his will, and wanted the mental examination in order to make it perfectly clear that he was sane so as to avoid legal complications for his family.

"It was clear to me he would not have been committed," Dr. Butler remembered. "Had he gone before the mental health commission, he would have denied what he told me. He told me he'd deny it all. This was such a philosophic, thought out decision, that there was no question he was in good order. I respect the concept of [withholding care] for those who are not subject to suicidal depression, who want to be released; their not wanting to go through massive surgery, or I.V.s, etc. But I want to make damn sure they know what they want. I'm very frightened of the example of Nazi Germany," said Dr. Butler. "There's going to be a reaction against Social Security beneficiaries, and people forget that about one quarter of them are not old people . . . . I predict we're going to have a revolt against Social Security, and we're going to push these people into death. We've already pushed them out of the job market . . . . There have been cases," he added, "of children who have brought plastic bags to their parents in nursing homes, left the bags on the bed and said, 'I thought you might want to use that.' "'

Two years ago, Dr. Butler told me he thought the Living Will was a "great" idea because "there are so many people who want to have a sense of having a voice" in their own life and death. But rather than urge persons to fill out Living Wills, those vague and therefore sinister documents that may ultimately condemn them to death rather than free them from prolonged dying, I believe we should be working to improve relations between patients and physicians. How much simpler to have an understanding with one's doctor and relatives rather than leave a set of irrevocable orders that may not fit the circumstances in which one finds oneself.

A prominent Washington, D.C., internist who asked that his name not be revealed told me of two patients with whom he had such a civilized arrangement. "I had one patient, a very intelligent woman in her seventies, who had terminal cancer and came to me on a special appointment to discuss the death problem. She said, 'I don't know whether you go along with this or not, but I wrote out my request in longhand. I want to know what your feeling is about it.' And she gave me the paper to read and it requested that in case she is unconscious at any time that I will promise her that I will not allow them to use 'heroic' means to keep her going when we know that it's hopeless. And I promised. She said, 'yes, but suppose you're out of town and someone else is taking your calls?' I said, 'I'll tell you what I'll do: I'll sign this note and I'll have it witnessed by my nurse who will be here if I'm away and it'll be filed with your chart and will be protected.' She was very happy. Consequently when she later became quite ill and became semicomatose, I went to the chart room at the hospital and made a note on her chart that she was not to 'be revived.' She died peacefully and I explained it to the friends and one relative who was a nurse.

"Now there have been other instances," the physician, himself an elderly man, told me, "where people have been hopelessly ill, comatose, and their wives have come to me and asked me whether I thought it was wise to continue transfusions and all the resuscitation efforts when there was absolutely no hope. And I agree with them that it is not . . . . There is one case I remember particularly," he continued. "A well known attorney here in town had a large blood clot on his brain. He was in a coma for three months, totally comatose, but the neurosurgeons kept working on him. I couldn't figure out why they were doing it, because I'd known the man and knew it wasn't the kind of thing he'd want. One day at the hospital, I ran into the man's wife. She asked to speak with me and I told her I was surprised she hadn't done so sooner. 'What are they doing to him?' she asked me. 'Why are they doing that? Can't they let him be be? Can't they stop and let him die?' I asked her why she hadn't spoken to the neurosurgeons," the physician explained, "and she said, I wouldn't know what to say to them.' I asked her if she wanted me to speak to the surgeons and she said she did, asking me to 'please tell them to stop.' I called the surgeons and said, 'hasn't he really been dead since the day you brought him in? There's no hope, is there? They told me there was no hope. 'Then what are you doing?'" the internist said he asked the surgeon. ' "I didn't want to take the responsibility of stopping,' the surgeon told me. 'I'll take it. Let him go.' They stopped and the man died. And every time the woman sees me, she thanks me for letting her husband die," the physician concluded.

10

I Can't Die Yet,
the Washing Isn't Caught Up!

Joy Ufema, nurse, ombudsman, comforter and friend of
the dying patients in the Harrisburg (Pa.) Hospital was
making her rounds one morning when she entered the room
of a new patient who had been told only two hours earlier
that he had prostate cancer. "What kind of work do you do,"
the man asked Joy, almost belligerently.

"I work with cancer patients," she replied. "How are
you feeling this morning? The doctors told you . . ."

"I feel fine," interrupted the man, brusquely. "I feel
fine." His unshaven face looked like a smudge on the white
hospital-issue pillowcase, and he did not look fine at all. He
looked, in fact, as though he were dying. And he was. But
until he died, Joy Ufema, one of the nation's first "death and
dying" nurses, would be there, ready to talk, ready to listen,
ready to give a back rub, and ready to just sit and hold the
hand of a very frightened fellow human being.

As the Harrisburg Hospital's "Nurse Specialist—Death and
Dying," a position she created for herself in 1973, Joy cares
for all the hospital's dying patients. She told me she asked for
the job after she came to the realization, along with many

others in the health-care field, that the medical professions have long ignored the needs of those whom they cannot save.

"Whomever Teaches People How to Die Teaches Them How To Live," reads the sign on the desk at which Joy sat as we talked about what she does and why she does it. "Damn it!" she exclaimed. "Can't we just do things naturally? Why do we need a specialist?" But she then proceeded to answer her own question by cataloging some of the little things she does and has done, things which hospitals with their rules and regulations have for many years forbidden. "Simple things, like getting the guy in room 10 a beer. Or I'll say, 'this guy has been in for 26 weeks, we want to get him outside.' But then some nurse will say, 'you have to ask the doctor,' and I'll say, 'no you don't,' and take him out."

Then there was the time when one of Joy's patients, who was dying of cancer, learned that her husband had been in an automobile accident and was also in the Harrisburg Hospital. The woman was frantic, Joy told me, "and I came in in my cowboy boots on my day off and took her up to his room, oxygen tank and all. She asked, 'could I have Harold in my room,' and I said, 'yes!' The nurses on the floor got all worked up, and I said, 'yes, men do stand up to pee. Can you handle that.' The physician brought him up to her room. Those two had breakfast together the next morning and she kept food down for the first time in three weeks."

Joy Ufema began nursing on a urology floor, "the floor where you wear the yellow shoes." Many of the patients on the floor were cancer patients, and she told me she began to realize that the dying patients were just never given enough time and attention. "You'd be talking with a dying patient and say, 'I'll be right back with you, Emily, I just have to go give these pills to Mrs. so-and-so and I'll be right back.' You'd come back and she'd be dead. I don't think hospitals are interested in the dying. We're life-saving institutions. We tend to isolate the individual [who is dying] within our society.

First we put them in a hospital or nursing home. Then we put them in a back room. There's an identification with death which most of us want to avoid," said Joy, who has cared for about 300 terminal patients.

Because she is attempting to make the last days of life easier for the hospital's dying patients, Joy Ufema often makes life rougher for the other nurses and doctors by breaking rules. "I find that people don't want to eat lunch with me," she told me. "I joke that they think I have this black cape and swoop into a patient's room and say, 'You're dying! You're dying! You're dying!' And then I swoop back out." The tall, angular woman dressed in regulation whites laughed at her own description of herself as the angel of death. "I never divulge to a patient the fact that the patient is dying," she told me, "but I do confirm" in a hospital where 60 to 70 percent of the time physicians do not tell their patients that they are dying. Joy's frankness does nothing to win her friends among physicians at the hospital. One doctor even went so far as to note on a patient's chart, "keep that death and dying squad out of my room!"

One of the reasons given for the supposed need for legalization of Living Wills is that patients become captives of the hospitals in which they find themselves. They are medically "seduced and abandoned." Long after there has ceased to be any hope for his patient, the physician treats her as though she were his sole reason for entering medical practice, and, indeed, she may be. For numerous studies have found that many young men and women become doctors out of a desire to overcome death either because they lost a parent or other family member at an early age or because of an inability to face their own mortality. They will, therefore, struggle against all odds to keep a patient alive. But once the battle against death is lost and the physician finally faces the inevitability of the patient's death, he often abandons the patient. Visits to the bedside become shorter and shorter, farther and farther apart. There never seems to be enough time to sit and talk. Never time to answer questions. Never enough time to respond to the dying person as a person. And that is where Joy Ufema comes in.

"I'm very comfortable with this work," Joy told me. "I believe dying patients are being abused. We're all human beings with human needs. Perhaps I'm just trying to bring a little dignity to people. I'll fight for those patients at the risk of loosing my job. Sure, I've blown some [cases]. Perhaps I've misidentified my motives and thought of what I'd want. The patient wants to go home to die and the wife says, 'no' and I say, 'shit! Can't you take it for two weeks? It's his turn now, it'll be your turn later.' " Joy paused for a moment, staring off into space. "Somedays I'm afraid to go down and fight those bitches," she said of her battling with other nurses. "But when I don't, I feel it when I leave. I'm sick of all this intellectualizing. If death is so groovey, why do we fight it with medicine?" asked Joy Ufema, who spends her days smuggling kittens in to a child dying of leukemia, or taking an old man outside for a last walk along the river, or arranging for a patient who has always bathed in the evening to bathe in the evening—despite hospital protocol which includes morning baths.

□

Jackie Ayre, 41, "a housewife and proud of it," mother of three teenagers, widow of a cancer victim and wife of a widower, considered Joy Ufema a friend. For Jackie, a victim of breast and bone cancer, spent a good deal of time in and out of the Harrisburg Hospital over the course of two years. And as Joy sat on Jackie's hospital bed, the two spoke as old friends, of children, laundry, and God.

"The children have matured greatly through this ordeal," Jackie told Joy Ufema, who asked how the children were doing. "They take care of the house, they do all the cooking, all the cleaning. They rotate. One takes care of the upstairs, one the downstairs, The 15-year old, Greg, made the whole Thanksgiving dinner. The only thing he needed help with [was his] lumpy gravy."

Jackie said her husband had been unemployed for 11 months, a victim of hard economic times. "We pray a lot," she told Joy and me. "He's had many offers, but they've entailed a move, or being on the road 100 percent of the time. It wasn't worth it. He's been a great help to me by being here. I think God has everything planned for," said Jackie Ayre, who then went on to say having cancer didn't bother her, in and of itself. "I wasn't sick, so I didn't think much of it. I was on my feet and continued my life style. It wasn't until my pins were knocked out from under me that my ego's hurt. I have to ask people to do things for me. I've been a proud, independent person."

"Are you angry, Jackie," asked Joy, who was sitting on Jackie's bed.

"I'm angry at the fact I can't do what I want to do. I'm terribly frustrated today because of this intravenous thing," she said, nodding toward the tube protruding from her arm.

"I haven't asked you this before Jackie," Joy said softly, "but when the end comes, do you have a preference where? Do you want it to be at home or here?"

"I don't know," said Jackie," who discussed the problem very matter-of-factly. "I don't know if I want my children there or not. My father died at home. My first husband died in the hospital. I wouldn't want my children to see me with a lot of tubes in me."

"You wouldn't have to have a lot of tubes and stuff," Joy told the woman.

"Then I'd rather die in the hospital," Jackie said, looking relieved.

The conversation turned back to Jackie's anger at her situation. "I'm a little angry with God right now," she told us. "I'm asking the question right now, why me? I've had my share of problems. It's time to get off my back and on to somebody else's."

The day I visited Jackie she had been in the hospital for three days. After three years of living with cancer, after two mastectomies and countless treatments, it looked as though she had entered the hospital for the last time. What, I asked, was she thinking about as she had returned to the hospital.

"I was thinking about what I was leaving behind," she told me. "I was thinking that I have a lot to do. When I came in to the hospital Friday, I thought 'this is it,' and I wasn't ready because I didn't have the washing done. Isn't that ridiculous? The washing wasn't caught up and I thought, 'Oh my God! I can't die yet, the washing isn't caught up.'" There were tears in her eyes as she tried to laugh, and there were tears in Joy Ufema's eyes, as the 32-year-old nurse tried soothingly to reassure Jackie that her concerns weren't "silly."

"But that was what was on my mind," Jackie insisted, "my family and what they're going to have to cope with without me. Even though I contribute little in activity to the home, at least the mother is still there."

"Oh yes, Jackie, that's very important," said Joy.

"At least the mother is still there. But that was my thought, that I hadn't finished the washing."

"You're needed, Jackie, you know that."

"It's so silly though," said Jackie Ayre, whose laughter couldn't quite make it through her tears. "Here you're going off to the hospital and you think you're going to die, and you've never felt so bad, and I was worried about the washing. But this is a mother. This is a housewife and mother talking."

☐

While it is never easy to work with dying patients, Joy Ufema says there is one group of patients with whom she has particularly difficult problems. This is the patient whom she calls the "52-year-old superman, this guy who's making $75,000 a year, sending a couple of kids to Harvard, the wife wears diamonds and rubbies, perfect make-up, a perfect facade, and she holds off the doctor and me. She tells the doctor, 'Now we don't want to tell Bill he's dying. He musn't know.' And she tells me to stay away from the room. But I sneak in there around 6:30 and there's Bill, bawling, and he asks, 'what's wrong with me? Am I dying?' Superman and his money can't buy new bone marrow. He feels like, 'I've controlled everything in my own life but now I can't control my own bladder.' "

Many of Joy's colleagues wonder how she can go on, working with the dying day after day, watching every one of her patients die. "It's a scary thing, man," she said to me. "Some days I'm afraid to die, some days I'm not. But we're all human needs. I'm going to die some day too, now what can I do to help you?"

But the rewards are often a great as the pains. There are the words and cards of thanks from families of patients. And smiles from patients. And things like the small pewter mug which sits on a shelf in her office, a gift from the 17 children of a woman who died of cancer. On the mug is inscribed the Biblical quotation: "Weeping may endure a night, but Joy cometh in the morning."

"That," said Joy Ufema, glancing at the mug, "was a good death, and I mean to use that word. Her family was with her through the vigil and with her when she died."

□

Dr. Nathan Schnaper has a little story he likes to tell that is probably apocryphal but which is worth pondering in light of all the current talk about "death with dignity," euthanasia, and "the right to die."

"There's a place down in Mexico," Dr. Schnaper told

me, "which serves meconium cocktails. They mix up the
meconium, [the feces in the intestinal tracts of infants at
birth] or maybe it's just a little dirt with fruit juice. The
stuff is supposed to help you live longer." Here Dr. Schnaper
paused, giving me a moment to wonder whether he was quite
serious. And then, "What that shows," he said, "is that
people will eat shit to stay alive." And Nathan Schnaper
should know. For Dr. Schnaper, a Baltimore psychiatrist, has
been working with terminally ill patients since the 1950s, and
during that time he has spoken with hundreds of persons who
wanted to live despite pain and physical deterioration.

Dr. Schnaper can be even more sure of what he says
because he has made what might be termed one-sided suicide
pacts with about 80 percent of the roughly 200 terminal
patients he has treated, but Nathan Schnaper said that not
one of the patients has ever called on him to follow through
by providing the patient with the means to commit suicide.

□

One of the patients with whom Dr. Schnaper made what
he calls his " 'implicit bargain'—the patient makes the deal, I
don't say anything," was a 20-year-old leukemic named Tom.
"When the time comes with Tom," Dr. Schnaper paused, "I
don't know what I'm going to do. Here's my prescription
pad." He tapped the pad on the table by his chair. "I'm not
discussing this with the Public Health Service doctors, who
are bound and determined they are going to do everything
possible to keep Tom alive no matter how painful it is and
how deteriorated he is. I guess I'm hoping that when the time
comes, even though we have an implicit bargain, that Tom
will be too sick to collect his IOU, too out of it. But if he's
not, and he says, 'this is the time,' will I write a prescription
for 50 Seconal for him?" Again, Dr. Schnaper paused, this
time for seven seconds . . . "I don't know. I guess what I

would do is write for the 50 Seconal and not give him the Seconal.

"It bothers me, I think it would bother me, if they said, 'he didn't die from his leukemia, he died from an overdose. The doctor gave him a prescription for 50 Seconal.' Even though I could argue and say, 'look, I didn't tell him to take them all at one time—' I think I would rather people—I don't know how I would handle it. I could give him the prescription in my own name for 50 Seconal. The pharmacist would look at me kind of funny, I might end up giving him the prescription, but I think the easiest way, to get around it, is to hand him the pills and say, 'Now Tom, one a night, it'll help you sleep.' He knows what to do with them."

"I justify it on moral and professional grounds," said Dr. Schnaper. "See, when the doctors are avoiding dying patients all the time, they don't get in at the end to give them something so they can go quickly, because they have been avoiding them all along. It's only those who are involved . . . . Now seeing these patients so-called psychiatrically, which is nonsense, it's a very private and particular relationship. You can say it's an emotional involvement if you want to. In these cases, I'm willing to help out. I justify it on my relationship, that this is a very dear friend. It makes it morally acceptable to me. Those who avoid the patient are never faced with this dilemma. It's difficult. It's wearying. When I saw Tom today, and he looked a little better, I was high.

"The issue to me, in this whole business, the whole issue is which is more difficult morally, to let somebody die an obscene, undignified, miserable, painful death, or to help them, in some way, die quickly when you know they have to die? To put it more succinctly, morally, the question is should we be more concerned about the quality of life or the so-called sanctity of biological life?" asked Nathan Schnaper.

"You know, my agreement with Tom came up again

today. I said, 'Tom, I don't know that you're ready for it, so don't ask me if I'm ready for it. Because sure as hell I'm not ready for it."

Nathan Schnaper never had to keep his implicit bargain with Tom, who lived for several months after Dr. Schnaper and I spoke. Dr. Schnaper told me that Tom was in great pain the day he died, but he never asked for the pills. Instead, he asked to be propped up in a wheelchair and taken out into the hospital corridor where he smoked his last cigarette. Later that same evening, Tom slipped into a coma and was dead by midnight.

"Has any patient ever asked you to follow through on your agreement," I asked Nathan Schnaper.

"They never do," he replied.

11

I Want to Die in This Bed!

Dimetro Kobylanski knew nothing of America's current facination with dying and death. The name Elisabeth Kubler-Ross meant nothing to him. And lecture circuit chatter about "death with dignity" would probably have left him bemused or disgusted. For Dimetro Kobylanski, a 76-year-old Ukranian immigrant factory worker knew enough about dying with dignity, to know that, like living with dignity, it is something one does, not something one talks about. And after one stay in the hospital for futile treatment of his esophageal cancer, he did not need to engage in a philosophical debate over whether he should return to the hospital to die. He simply refused to go back. He knew that another stay in the hospital would mean lying in his own private hell, moaning and whimpering with pain as he waited for the nurse to bring him his medication according to her schedule. He knew the hospital was a place where he went to the bathroom when it was his turn, not when he needed to go. So he stayed at home, with Polin, his wife of 40 years, in the tiny front room of their third story walkup in New Haven, Connecticut's blue-collar Fairhaven section. His last days were spent on a rented hospital bed, in his own home, surrounded by the people he loved and the few possessions he had accumulated during a lifetime of hard work. With his daughter-in-law, Irene Kobylanski, translating his Ukranian into heavily accented English, Dimetro Kobylanski told me that "he don't want to go to the hospital. He knows they not going to help him any more in the hospital. He say he want to die at home." At that point her father-in-law shakily propped up himself on one elbow and said with surprising vehemence, "I want to die in this bed!"

"He's not afraid to die, like he said," Irene translated. "But he needs at least something to help him with the pain. And that's what you people help with, the pain." At that point she was talking to Dr. Sylvia Lack, who was sitting on the edge of Dimetro Kobylanski's bed, holding his hand.

Like Mr. Kobylanski, Dr. Lack's other patients do not get well, but they do die well. For Sylvia Lack is one of a small but growing number of concerned persons who have found the incredibly simple answer to the seemingly perplexing question of how to deal with the terminally ill; and that is to deal with them as the unique human beings they have been all their lives. This treatment of the dying patient is based on the belief that the dying person is just that, a *person* who happens to be dying and not an object for medical experimentation, abuse, or, even more common and even worse, neglect. Dr. Lack's patients may suffer the ravages of terminal cancer, but they do not lie forgotten in hospital wards, their collapsing veins jammed with intravenous needles, as they wait in agony for some overworked nurse to bring the next dose of pain killer. They do not suffer the useless indignity of being mauled and manhandled as a team of specialists attempts to revive them after their hearts give out, only to "save" them for a few more days of agony.

Dr. Lack is the medical director of the New Haven Hospice, an institution dedicated to the very sensible proposition that one's last days should not be wasted on dying but rather should be used to live until one dies. Traditionally, the word hospice has been used to refer to a resting place for travelers. But since the establishment in 1967 of St. Christopher's Hospice, in London, it has become more than likely that a person speaking of a hospice is referring to a hospital, or home, exclusively for the dying and incurably ill, a place where schedule and regimen are established to fit the needs of the individual patient rather than to a place where the patient is made to fit the mold of the institution. The hospice patient is not simply another battlefield in the medical sciences, eternal war against the death of the dying. Rather, he is a person whom the institution's staff recognizes is near death and whose last days of life those staff members—nurses, doctors, secretaries, receptionists, and social workers—attempt to make as fulfilling as possible. That is not to say that the staff attempts to force the patient to be more active than the patient is capable of being. Nor does the staff seek to delude the patient with a sense of false hope. But it does mean that the patient is kept as free from pain as is humanly possible, and in the majority of cases, that freedom from debilitating pain is accomplished without doping the patient insensible.

As she sat beside him on his bed, Sylvia Lack asked Dimetro Kobylanski to describe the kind of pain he experienced prior to admission into the hospice home care program. "It's like a fire inside," Irene Kobylanski said, translating her father-in-law's Ukranian. "If somebody put a hot iron on your hand, on your skin, that's the pain he feels inside." Dr. Lack said that when she first visited Mr. Kobylanski he remained curled in a fetal position, moaning, clutching a hot water bottle to his chest for the entire time of her visit. But when she and I visited the home, Dimetro Kobylanski was being given morphine in large enough doses, frequently enough, so that he was not in serious pain. "The goal of the home care program at the moment is to achieve a situation where pain is no longer a problem," said Dr. Lack,

who came to the New Haven program from St. Christopher's.
"One patient said to me, 'I've got head pain, I've got chest
pain, leg pain, stomach pain. I'm just pain all over.' And
when you get these people so that they are in fact relating
and talking to their families again and are beginning to take
up some of their daily activities, within the limitations of
their illness, and they no longer start talking about pain the
minute you walk in, but talk about other things, that's when
pain is no longer a problem."

While heroin is the pain killer of choice in the British
hospices, its use in this country is precluded by law. Instead,
patients in the hospice program in New Haven are given
morphine, a heroin derivative which researchers have found
to be as effective as heroin in the control of pain if the doses
are large enough and frequent enough. While many physicians
condemn their terminal patients to seemingly interminable
pain and suffering because the doctors are afraid their
patients may become drug addicts, Dr. Lack neither fears
the specter of addiction nor finds that her patients become
addicted. In her work both in England and New Haven, she
has found, as have some other physicians, that if narcotics are
administered often enough and in sufficiently large amounts
to insure that the patient does not experience a period of
pain between doses, there is no psychological addiction.
Psychological addiction, which is a far greater problem than
physical addiction, is caused, say the physicians I have
spoken to, by the craving the patient develops as he or she
struggles through the long minutes or hours of pain between
doses of medication. If the patient has to wait for the
narcotic, the patient's thinking about the relief from pain and
the fear that he will not be granted that relief make him
psychologically dependent upon the agent providing the
relief. Obviously, even if there is no psychological addiction,
the patient may become physically addicted to narcotics.
However, if the patient is lucky enough to experience a

remission of the disease, or is somehow cured, physicians say the physical addiction is relatively easy to cure by slowly reducing the doses.

The New Haven Hospice, the nation's first, does not yet have an inpatient facility. As of this writing, it is strictly a home care program, funded by a contract with the National Cancer Institute and foundation grants. Ultimately, the hospice will care for about 100 home care patients and 44 inpatients in an ultramodern facility to be constructed in Branford, Connecticut, just outside New Haven. The institution's goal is to provide the support and encouragement families need to be able to keep their terminally ill relatives at home, if that is where the patient wants to be. The inpatient facility will provide a homelike atmosphere for those patients who either do not want to or cannot die at home for various reasons. Like St. Christopher's Hospice in England, the Branford Hospice will be an open, cheerful, place, where all family members, including young children and pets, are welcome. Patients will be allowed to bring some of their own furniture and possessions with them and will even be given a choice of colorful materials for the curtains around their beds. There will be a day care center/nursery for staff members that will insure there will usually be children in the building, helping to belie the hospice image of a house of death. The plans for the facility include only four private rooms; all other patients will share four-bed rooms to encourage communication and sharing among patients and, hopefully, to prevent the dying patients from becoming isolated. Because the facility will not be filled with expensive, ultrasophisticated medical equipment, patients will pay about one half the amount they would pay in a New Haven area acute-care hospital.

But all that is still many months in the future. In the mean time, the hospice home care team—two physicians, seven nurses, a social worker, a psychiatric consultant, and about 45 volunteers—ministers to about 35 terminal cancer patients and the survivors of about another 20 former hospice patients. The patients and families are referred to the hospice by private physicians, hospitals, and social service agencies. Interestingly, 77 patients, or 57 percent of 136 recent referrals to the program came from 77 physicians, who each referred one patient. "What this demonstrates," Sylvia Lack told me, "is that hospice gets the worst patients, the ones no one else can handle."

□

She was attractive. The mother of two teenage daughters. And she was dying of cancer. She was thin, but not as thin as she pictured herself. With full make-up and her hair carefully washed and brushed, she lay in bed in a pretty dressing gown. Smoking. She spoke for over an hour to Patti Rout, the 28-year-old hospice nurse assigned to her case. It was a harrowing hour—a gray blur. But a few moments stand out.

*

"I'm so angry I could just scream," she said, carefully watching Patti's face to see her reaction.

"You should," Patti told her.

*

"Patti, what's it like to die?"

"I don't know."

"But have patients told you, at the end?"

"They said it's very peaceful."

"That's what I've read," said the woman, who turned away from Patti and stared thoughtfully at the ceiling.

*

"I'm not a wife any more."

*

"If I didn't believe in an afterlife I'd go crazy."

*

"My husband gets so angry at times he can tear the house down. . . . He said, I'd rather have you like this for ten years than not have you . . . "

"What did you say," asked Patti.

"I told him I couldn't go through this for ten years."

*

"My daughter said, 'Mom, I wish you'd died when you had your hysterectomy, so I'd be all over missing you.' I tell ya Patti, that hurt."

*

"Couldn't I just see my daughters get married? This is the fullest time of my life. My daughters are getting to be independent. My husband and I have time to do some things. Why do I have to die?"

*

The following afternoon I sat in on the home care team's daily afternoon report period. Patti had left her notebook at the woman's house and had to make a second visit the day we had been there. It was a visit which had left her a wreck. "I went back out last night again," she told her colleagues," and there was lots of crying and depression and stuff. She is contemplating not going back in for chemo [therapy]. She and her family are discussing it. I really feel the need for someone, I mean myself, to get into some kind of really aggressive therapy for the whole family. They said the daughter is so depressed she hasn't been out of her nightgown in three days, she won't go out with her sister to restaurants, you know, to lunch. This is certainly a case of depression, and she's saying things like, 'Patti, tell me just how it's going to be when I die. Why is it taking me so long to die?' And her daughter said to her, 'Mommy, I wish you had died when you went in for your last operation because then it would be all over with you now.' And her husband told me last night that he'd like to put a gun to his head and go into the grave with her."

"So you smiled," quipped another nurse.

"Oh, patience *is* a virtue," said another.

"It's just really bad," said Patti. "I mean, it's the whole family and you can just say so much to them." The situation was clearly getting to her.

"And they're talking this way all the time at home," asked the social worker.

"Yeah. It kind of bothers me when it gets to the point where it's preventing them from doing any kind of functioning, whether it's going out to lunch or doing anything. I don't think the kids are in on this, but Mr. and Mrs. are. She asked him yesterday how he felt about her dying in the bed and what kind of effect it would have afterwards. And he said, well, he does think he could handle it but he's not sure the girls can. You know, he's just really down. He has no support system at all. His family is supportive in that they're there all the time, but he said they walk in, take one look at him or his wife and burst into tears and go out in the garage and cry. He has no one to talk to at work. There's no one there that he can . . ." Patti stopped to collect her breath and light another cigarette. "He went to the church, and the priest was giving a sermon on Christ's suffering, and he had the priest come to the house because that really angered him, you know. He said, 'fine, Christ only suffered for three days. He carried the cross and then was dead. My wife has been suffering for two and one-half years and it's still not over.' It's just like, you know . . ."

Joan Quarberg, the chief of nursing interrupted, "It's interesting though that the priest came out to talk about it."

"Yeah, he did. [The husband] called the priest and told him that he was so angered by the sermon that he just about burst and he was going to stand up and yell in church. And the priest came out and spent a long time talking with him."

"With her too?" asked the social worker.

"He visited with her too. They really like this priest and feel they have a good relationship." But Patti then went on to explain to the team that the husband and wife were frustrated by their church, "because they feel that they've asked the questions that they want to ask and nobody has any answers. 'This is life and it's rotten and it's unjust and God isn't right.' But you know, she said she might call him again, but I don't think anybody's gonna tell her husband anything that's gonna . . . You know, he said, 'the only thing I want to hear is that my wife isn't going to die.' And she said yesterday that she isn't even a wife any more. So we went into this thing about positions, and different ways of showing your affection, whether you actually perform the [sex] act or not. It was such an improvement that I felt like singing. Then I went back last night and saw her in the family constellation and saw him sitting at the table bawling. It's just so far out. I mean, they don't want to have sex. They're depressed and worried about her dying and it just seemed like such a dumb thing to have discussed sex. But at the time . . . . It's just depressing. It really is. I don't know what we do, whether we need more counseling, whether we need psychiatric help out there or . . ." Patti, a young woman generally in complete control of herself and the situations in which she finds herself, seemed to be hitting a brick wall. What do you do?

"Well, maybe it would help for you to talk to our psychiatric consultant to see, you know, present all this to him and see where we go," suggested the social worker. "And the other thing I think about Patti is, really, I don't know if those girls are going to handle it. Each of those school systems . . ."

"The girl that's really depressed is out of school," interjected Patti. "She finished up an early program so she had her credits in December or January and doesn't graduate until June."

"So she's home?"

"Yeah. all the time. The husband said his family is very good and when his wife dies they'll just come over and sit around the house and cry together for a week. But he said he has no reason to go on living."

"But he does though," Joan said.

"Well," continued Patti, "he said, 'outside of the girls I have no reason to go on living. If it wasn't for the girls I'd just blow my brains out and go in the grave with her.' "

"I don't know," Joan said. "It just seems to me we've got to hang on there somehow; listen to him but not get too overwhelmed."

"It sounds O.K. when you're sitting here," replied Patti.

"I know," Joan said quietly.

"But when you're out there, it gets to you."

"Is there anyway I can help," asked Dr. Richard Glendon, a hospice physician.

"Yeah, well I said to him last night, when I asked him about his support, you know, 'is there anyone at work you can talk to,' I asked, 'would you feel better if one of our male staff members came out here and maybe you could share different kinds of, you know, show your anger, or get it out differently, if there was someone other than myself,' " continued Patti. "And he said, 'oh, nothing's going to help; nothing's going to help.' And I said, 'Dr. Glendon might come out to see you,' and he said, 'not unless he has a miracle cure,' You know, it's just . . . "

"How about a volunteer thing," asked the social worker, referring to the extensive volunteer program run by the hospice, the possibility of assigning a male volunteer to the home.

"I just don't know," replied Patti, "I really don't. You know, others are going into the home beside myself, because I'm taking a weekend off. But I guess, just as long as I come back here and battle at the mouth about it . . . . "

"Can I be of any help directly, with the girls or somebody else," wondered the social worker.

"I don't know, I really don't know," Patti repeated. "I said to the husband yesterday that I'd like to come out and sit down with the two girls and have a talk with them, and his wife said she really appreciated that. And I know I've told her a thousand times, and other people have said it to her, but yesterday was the first day she *heard* that we followed the family afterwards [through its period of bereavement and adjustment following the death] and that was of some positive strength to her. She mentioned it again last night and she said, 'boy, are you going to have your work cut out for you once I'm gone. My family is really going to need you.' She said that in front of her husband. So I guess that's really something, but . . . . "

The social worker then asked when Patti would next visit the family and said she would wait to meet the family until Patti could introduce her. "I'd rather go with you," she said, "because you know them best." And the group moved on to a discussion of another patient.

While many social service agencies provide the services provided by the hospice, they provide the services on a very fragmentary basis with one group providing nursing care, another providing counseling, another providing homemaking assistance, and yet another helping the family deal with its creditors. No one agency coordinates the various services, and few, if any, tell a family about the other agencies which are available to help. And one of the unique and most important features offered by the hospice is that the various support services are available to the patient and family before the need for those services becomes critical and the situation is beyond control. As was the case with the family discussed in the meeting, the nurse who visits the home on a regular basis can observe the family and call on the experience and expertise of the other members of the hospice team as soon as she sees any problems developing.

That expertise is largely the result of on-the-job training, for as Sylvia Lack told me,"Ordinary people are the people to do this work . . . . Essentially, you learn about how to care for dying patients from the dying patients themselves. Our nurses, obviously, are given basic orientation and all the rest of it. But essentially the important thing is that they just go into each situation with all their senses coming out to pick up what the right thing to do is. You know, there's no set technique. Terminal care is not done by a cookbook. It's not like doing an operation, where you've got set procedures," said Dr. Lack, who trained under Dr. Cicely Saunders, the guiding spirit behind St. Christopher's and the entire hospice movement. "What's entirely appropriate in one situation may be entirely inappropriate in another," said Dr. Lack. "And you just have to train people to have very sharp ears, because you're going to tell them to play it by ear."

You also have to wonder about the nurses. About their sensibilities and, ultimately, their sanity. Why, you wonder, would a young woman who could work in any of the countless areas of nursing choose to work for a place like a hospice, where the patients always die, where no matter how hard you work and care no one ever gets better?

Often, like Patti Rout, they come to the hospice out of frustration at their inability to really help terminal patients in the traditional hospital setting. Patti, who was one of the original nurses at the New Haven Hospice and, in fact, was part of the task force which developed the hospice concept, remembers "sitting on the edge of a patient's bed in a four-bed room [in the Yale-New Haven Hospital]. . . ." He was a cardiac patient, and they have the same fears as anyone else . . . . But in an acute-care hospital you're not allowed to sit on a bed. You are not allowed to hold the hand of a patient. You don't have the time. You have to be busy, you see, busy doing something physical. So, a nurse came into the room and at first glance I thought it was my supervisor who had just returned from a visit to St. Christopher. But it was only my friend Shirley, and she said, I've got to tell you about this great new kind of nursing where you're allowed to sit and you're supposed to do it. And that's how I got interested. Because I thought you should have a right to sit and listen to a patient's fears, no matter what they are, what kind of patient, particularly with a dying patient, and I really felt the need for this new group that was starting on this hospice, and the more I stayed with them the more I was convinced that this had to be an alternative.

"I don't think we make dying easy. I really don't especially as you've seen in the last few days. To evaluate what we're doing, the only thing I can go home and ask is, have I enabled the family to raise the level of contentment in their house. That's really my main objective, to really give of myself. To give something, no matter what it is, and I think that's why our program is so different; it's not necessarily based on your best nursing skills. I mean they're needed, you have to have them, but if that isn't what the patient needs, you listen to the patient's needs and you give them what they need. Give of yourself, your time, that's what you give. I just want to come out of there thinking that I gave something to raise the level of contentment in that house. And that can be in very physical care, colostomy care, and these horrendous wounds that we take care of. As you've seen, in many cases I'm doing physical care when I go into a home. But I really came to the hospice because of a need that I saw that wasn't being . . . . and there are many needs . . . because it's one that I was interested in."

"But how do you deal with it, day after day, knowing that everyone you touch is going to turn to dust. Nobody gets better?"

"Because there's a satisfaction in it. I mean you get your satisfaction from seeing the good that you can do, knowing that if this patient was left in a hospital or a convalescent

home they wouldn't have gotten three quarters of the
care . . . . If their main wish is to stay at home, you're
enabling them to do that. They might still have the pain or
discomfort, and they're still dying, but you're giving them
something that they want. They want to stay at home. It gets
depressing. It's hard. You grieve with the family when you
lose someone, and this isn't a plug for what we're doing, but
you couldn't do it without the team. We have just fantastic
support here. There's always someone that's here to pitch in
with you if you need the help . . . . It does get depressing but
not frustrating. You still have frustrations, but you have a
team behind you that understands. I mean, you know at
work in a hospital, there's no way that anybody would have
listened to me for that last half hour, talking about how I'm
having difficulties coping with the family and how I can help
this family. You get three minutes to report in a hospital.
They don't want to hear about personal problems. Was he
out of bed? Did he have a bath? Did he move his bowels?
That's it. A.M. care given."

"Do you ever get too involved with a family?"

"This is a very personal opinion. You'll get many
different versions. But I don't believe you can get too
involved."

"But can't you lose your perspective on what's happening in the household?"

"Yes. You can. You can get so involved with one
particular area of a problem that you do lose your objectivity
in other areas, but that's something that . . . so you think
about the team. That's why no one person is ever the only
one going into a particular home, you know, for one reason
or another, either we're going to plan it that way or it's going
to happen that way because of scheduling. That's the team
concept. The family knows it. There's always someone else
going in. It might be only once a month or once every five
visits of mine, but there's going to be a check up system.

There's going to be somebody else going in who's fresh to the situation, who's going to pick up on it. But you can get very involved without losing your objectivity, as I am with alot of my patients."

"How do you not take it home with you at night?"

"I'm not sure you don't. I couldn't ever say you don't take it home."

"Then what happens to your personal life? What happens to your family?"

"That's one of the big things when you're hired here. To be hired they really check you out very carefully. Do you have an outside support system? Do you have friends other that at the hospice, so that when . . . so that in your own personal life you're not constantly talking about the hospice, because that seems to happen around here an awful lot. I always say my three-year-old is my break from reality. I can go home sad, or just leaving a death, but he's still there. He's still going to do crazy things and make me laugh and I get caught up in my own life. But I'm still on call. And even though I might be functioning around the house as a housewife, a wife, a mother, a friend, whatever, I'm still on call. So in the back of my mind, if that phone rings, I have to break from what I'm doing and zero in on my work. I don't think you can be involved with a dying patient and not think about it. But you don't preoccupy your time. I still go out and party. I still go on vacations. I still take weekends off. I'm still a wife and mother. It's not that you're preoccupied with them, but you do have a responsibility to know what's happening and to be able to, in the middle of the night, be able to get up and function if they call. But you have to work very actively at not letting it become your whole life."

The best way to understand and appreciate the work done by the hospice is to speak to patients like Dimetro Kobylanski and their families and to talk to the survivors of the hospice patients, as I did when I accompanied Dr. Lack on a bereavement visit to the home of Albert and Eleanor Gustauskas. One of the first thing the Gustauskases told me was how much better they felt about the death of Mr. Gustauskas' father because they had, with the help of the hospice, made it possible for him to die at home.

"His wish was always, 'I want to be at home,' " said Eleanor Gustauskas, "and we promised faithfully that we would leave him at home; we would take care of him. And the hospice gave us more and more help as he got sicker. They were with us constantly. I think it would have broken his heart much sooner" to have been institutionalized, Eleanor said.

"You know, one thing with a patient of that type, terminally ill, is the hospital doesn't want to have anything more to do with them because there is nothing they can do for them," Albert said of his father. "All they can do is just change bandages and so on, which they feel somebody else can do, so they don't want them in the hospital. And a convalescent home doesn't want them because they feel, 'this person is too sick, he's not going to recover, and he requires more care than say a person with a broken leg.' So you're sort of in between both of them. And the hospice, I'd say, was a lifesaver, not a lifesaver, but a helping hand between the hospital and the convalescent home."

"That's very good, and it's an interesting way of putting it, that we were a lifesaver, most people think of the program and would not use the term lifesaver," said Dr. Lack.

"You are," said Eleanor Gustauskas, "because when father was sick, and he was very sick in March and April, he started to feel better because all the hospice nurses had been encouraging him and by encouraging him he got better, just enough to enjoy his garden in the summertime. And you said, come September, he will start to fail, be prepared. And if we didn't have this, I think . . . . We knew he was dying, but it's like a child, you have to have someone say, 'this is all right, this is to be expected.' We weren't getting that from the [hospice] doctors, but we were getting it from all the girls [hospice nurses] who came to see him: 'this is going to happen, don't worry about it, we'll be here.' And they sort of prepared us. Even though we knew that the end was coming, it was alot easier to carry because somebody gave us answers. They all said, 'call, it doesn't matter what time it is, call. Even if you just want somebody to talk to, call. And somebody will talk to you.' "

The Gustauskases told me that because of the help they received from the hospice, they were able to get the rest they needed, as well as the occasional bit of detachment one has to have to hold together, to be able to be of real help to Albert's father. "We had an occasion to go on a vacation during that summer," said Albert, "and we were kind of skeptical about going, as far as his condition was—we didn't know when the end would come and so on—and we were encouraged to go by the hospice; 'don't worry about him, he isn't quite in that stage, so go ahead and take a vacation because probably later on you won't be able to take it.' So we went down to North Carolina and they came in to see him everyday."

The couple reminisced with Dr. Lack for about 45 minutes until, without Dr. Lack having said anything intentionally to direct the conversation, the Gustauskases began to speak about the problem of how to discuss Andrew Gustauskas' death with his three-year-old great-grandson and namesake, Andrew.

"I don't know what my daughter-in-law has said to him," Eleanor told Dr. Lack.

"It's important that she does say something to him directly," Sylvia said. "It's very important that she sits down and says something to him. He needs to be told. And I would not say that God took him, because he may be angry with God, or frightened. You can tell him that he's gone to God, or something . . . and that we're all very sad that he's not here anymore, and in some way make it O.K. for him to be sad. And if he wants to cry, that's O.K. . . . we're sad that he's not here, but he was old and he's gone to God. And that's the way things are."

"I would have said he's too little yet," said Eleanor. "He used to go right into the bedroom and say, 'gate gandpa, you taking a nap again?' and my poor father-in-law would look up and he'd hold out his hands, as weak as he was, and we'd pick him up and put him down and he'd give him a big kiss. And he'd say 'Mathew not taking a nap,' and he'd go out. That's true. And he knows the house. The minute you stop the car he knows whose house it is."

"But don't be too worried what you do and say to him," said Dr. Lack. "The most important thing is to say something. And if he cries, let him cry. 'We're all sad that he's not here anymore. And we all cry. But when people get old that's what happens.' "

"They got left with good memories instead of getting left with the bad," Dr. Lack told me after our visit to the Gustauskas'. "That's not always true, and in bereavement time you may have to listen to alot of bad memories and problems. But very often it's . . . I think one of one's aims is to have the family left with good memories. . . . "

AFTERWORD

Almost all of us want to live, and very few of us want to die.

While that is hardly a profound observation, it is something which we should start giving a great deal of thought to immediately. Dying and death are not simply abstract processes to be read about and discussed for a few hours and then forgotten. They are, instead, a part of life which we all must face someday. How we think about them now may, in large measure, determines how we will face them when the time comes. In this age of medical miracles and eternal life, it is entirely possible that any one of us could end his or her days as Karen Ann Quinlan. It is even more likely that some of us will find ourselves in Stanley Levey's slippers or making the kind of decisions made by the parents about whom you read.

We must consider these problems now, for once we are personally confronted by them, it will certainly be too late to reach objective conclusions and solutions, and it may be impossible to reach any decision at all. If we do not thoroughly discuss with our families and physicians now our views of dying, death, and useless prolongation of life, we have no right to expect that they will do for us what we would do for ourselves. We should choose our physicians with some thought as to how they will minister to us when we are dying and beyond the reach of their technicial skills, as well as with thought to the quality of those skills.

The very fact that there is a Joy Ufema is a cultural disgrace, for all nurses, in all hospitals, should be Joy Ufemas. Caring for the dying must become an integral part of caring for the living, for the dying are living until they are dead. And there should be no need for hospices, for every home should be a hospice for the members of the family who live in that home. Until we do something to realize these very simple ideals—and doing something requires a change in attitude, not a change in laws—the dying will continue to be relegated to the rooms farthest from the nursing stations and parents like Joseph and Julia Quinlan will be forced to go to court to confront a society which so fears death that it refuses to accept its inevitability.

INDEX

Abramson, David 114 fol.
Addiction 186
Alcohol 10, 51, 70
Anencephalic monster 105, 106
Anglo-Saxon law 59
Armstrong, Paul 59, 63
Avery, Gordon 109, 115 fol.
Ayre, Jackie 176
Benton, Jesse 52
Berlin, Donald L. 19, 21
Brain stem preparation 52, 60
Branford (Conn.) Hospice 187
Butler, Robert N. 170 fol.
Calcagno, Philip 115
Campbell, A.G.M. 113
Catholic Church: see Roman
    Catholic Church
Children's Hospital National
    Medical Center 109, 115
Chubb & Son, Inc. 52
Church: see Roman Catholic
    Church
Coburn, Daniel 10, 105
Connery, John 57, 58
Constitutional rights 36
Cowley, R. Adams 79, 87 fol.
Crowley, James 59, 60
Death redefined 52, 53
Death with dignity 61 fol., 166
Diamond, Sidney 30
Drugs: see Heroin; Morphine;
    Tranquillizers
Duff, Raymond S. 113
Euthanasia 55, 56
    Trapasso 22
    Quinlan case 55
Euthanasia, Passive 55

Euthanasia Education Council 160
Extraordinary means 58
Frankenstein 67, 68
Frankenstein, Victor 68
Geeks and Gorks 130
George Washington University
    Medical Center 72 fol.
Georgetown University 57
Georgetown University Medical
    Center 114
Gill, William 77 fol., 82, 87 fol.
Glendon, Richard 192
Great Oaks (Md.) 121
Gude, Gilbert 121
Gustauskas, Albert and Eleanor 198
Hannan, Susan 80, 81
Harrisburg Hospital 173
Hellegers, Andre 164
Heroin 186
Hippolito, Ernest 75, 76, 81
Hospices movement 184 fol., 194 fol.
Hughes, Richard J. 54, 55, 62
Hyrdocephalic infants 119 fol.
Infants, Defective 107 fol.
Javed, Arshad 20, 34, 35, 52
Jehovah's Witnesses 108
Kennedy Institute for the Study of
    Human Reproduction and Bio-
    ethics 57, 164
Kobylanski, Dimetro 183
Korein, Julius 105
Lack, Sylvia 184 fol.
Lakeland Rescue Squad 69
Levey, Nan 143 fol.
Levey, Robert 142 fol.
Levey, Stanley 142 fol.
Librium 10

Living Will 159
Lucas, Ted 112
McAslan, T. Crawford 86 fol., 124
Malpractice suits 52, 53
Maryland Institute for Emergency Medicine 47, 74, 79
Medical technology 11, 21, 51, 69
  costs 60, 79, 91
Medvac 74, 76
Mercy killing
  Trapasso 22
  see also Euthanasia
Milhorat, Thomas Herrick 110
Mongolism 109
Monsters 69, 71, 105, 106, 107
Morphine 186
Morris View Nursing Home 19, 20, 22
Morse, Robert 20, 35, 85
Muir, Robert, Jr. 24, 50, 54
Nansen, Meredythe L. 19
New Jersey Superior Court 10,20, 50, 85
New Jersey Supreme Court 19, 20, 24, 54, 62
New Haven Hospice 184, 187
Newton Memorial Hospital 10, 26, 29, 70
Nurse Specialist—Death and Dying 173
Our Lady of the Lake Church 21, 35
Palmer, Peggy 75, 76, 83
Porzio, Ralph 50, 52
Potter, John 167
Pius XII 58
Quality of life 53, 56

Quarberg, Joan 190
Quinlan, John 11
Quinlan, Joseph Thomas 11, 19, 24 fol., 30 fol.
Quinlan, Julia 11, 19, 25 fol., 30 fol.
Quinlan, Karen Ann
  cause of coma 9, 10,11, 29
  Newtown Memorial Hospital 10, 70
  treatment cost 60
Quinlan, Mary Ellen 11, 26
Rath, Charles 168
Right to Life society 100
Roman Catholic Church 36 fol., 57 fol.
Roman law 59
Rosewood 111
Rout, Patti 188
Saint Christopher's Hospice 185
St. Clare's Hospital 20, 71
Saunders, Cicely 194
Schnaper, Nathan 87, 88, 91, 93, 96, 97, 179 fol.
Shelley, Mary Wollstonecraft 67, 68
Shock Trauma Unit 47, 74 fol.
Solomon, Louis 80, 81
Sugarman, Helene and Joel 119 fol.
Suicide 169, 170
Teague, Kay and Michael 109
Tranquilizers 51, 70
  see also Librium; Valium
Trapasso, Father 19, 21, 36, 59
Ufema, Joy 173
Valium 10
Ward, Susan 162
Watson, Richard 19
Why Survive? Being Old in America 170
Zimmerman, Jack 72, 73

174
C   Colen, B. D.

      Karen Ann Quinlan

W'97

DATE			

© THE BAKER & TAYLOR CO.